# TECHNIQUES OF
# GLASS MANIPULATION
## in Scientific Research

Simple portable pumping station.   See Chapter XI.

# TECHNIQUES OF

# GLASS MANIPULATION

## in Scientific Research

by

## JULIUS D. HELDMAN, Ph. D.

CHEMISTRY DEPARTMENT AND THE RADIATION LABORATORY
UNIVERSITY OF CALIFORNIA

New York

PRENTICE-HALL, INC.

PRENTICE-HALL CHEMISTRY SERIES
WENDELL M. LATIMER, PH. D., *Editor*

COPYRIGHT, 1946, BY

PRENTICE-HALL, INC.

70 Fifth Avenue, New York

First Printing..........March, 1946
Second Printing........August, 1947

PRINTED IN THE UNITED STATES OF AMERICA

To My Wife

# Preface

THIS book is designed for the technician, the chemist, the biologist, the physicist, and all others who at some time find it desirable to repair breaks in glass apparatus or to fabricate not-too-complicated pieces of glass equipment. Many large universities and industrial laboratories have professional glass blowers who construct intricate and esthetically pleasing glass apparatus; to these men a simple repair or construction is a matter of a few minutes' work, and the result is a neat and smoothly finished job. On the other hand, many research institutions do not have a glass-blowing shop, so that the technician is often called upon to make necessary repairs himself. And, even though a professional glass blower is available, it is often much quicker and just as satisfactory for the research worker to make his own mercury-sealed stirrer or even an all-glass distilling apparatus than to go through the routine of the glass shop. In vacuum work it is certainly necessary for the chemist or physicist to make additions and changes on the vacuum bench with some degree of proficiency.

It has been the author's observation that the greatest hindrance to the successful teaching of a technical subject is language block—the use of terms familiar to the teacher or writer but foreign to the student or reader. For this reason, a glossary of terms has been included, so that the proper technical terms used in the book may be at once referred to and understood.

The fundamental operations are given extra emphasis, for two reasons: (1) They are the ones most often encountered, and (2) technicians who have really mastered them are ready to try more extended manipulations with less detailed description of them. The basic principles of metal-to-glass sealing are also heavily stressed, because any book that is designed for self-instruction must leave no fundamental hiatus, whereas an incomplete textbook can be filled out by supplemental lectures and demonstrations. It should not be inferred, however, that unsupported self-instruction in glass blowing is desirable. As in all other manipulative skills, demonstration is the most powerful teaching tool, and every effort should be made to watch competent glass blowers at work.

Predominance has been given to the glass that is rapidly displacing others in laboratory use—namely, Pyrex No. 774.[1] Very few pieces of bench-blown equipment are made from anything but 774 in this country now, so that 774 technique is justly stressed in any work intended as a guide for laboratory workers.

Glass and fire are fascinating subjects. It would be impossible to include, in a book the size and scope of this one, any detailed discussion of the material outlined in Chapters I and II from the standpoint of practical utility, or to include a bibliography of published work on the subjects. Those who are particularly interested will seek further on their own initiative, but it will be worth while to mention two books on glass here. Morey, George W., *Properties of Glass*, Reinhold Publishing Co., New York, 1938, is an exhaustive critical compendium of published fundamental research on glasses, embracing all of their chemical and physical properties; and Phillips, C. J., *Glass: The Miracle Maker*, Pitman Publishing Co., New York, 1941, gives an over-all picture of the versatility of glasses, their uses, and their possibilities. In addition, Strong, J., *Procedures in Experimental Physics*, Prentice-Hall, Inc., New York, 1944, is an outstanding book dealing in part with glass manipulation in the laboratory, and should be consulted for discussion of such operations as polishing and techniques in high-vacuum work, both of which are treated in greater detail than is possible in the present work.

The author is indebted to a number of people who, consciously or unconsciously, contributed to the background that made the writing of this book possible. Without the author's

---

[1] See Glossary, Part A.

wife, to whom the book is dedicated and who critically read the original manuscript from the standpoint of the reader unacquainted with technical terminology, as well as offering much-needed encouragement and suggestions and typing the various drafts, the book would certainly never have been completed.   Among the glass blowers it has been the author's pleasure to know, Adrian van Tijn Jannse, Walter Cummings, and especially Harry Powell have unwittingly contributed many of the details that make up glass-blowing technique.

Discussions with Dr. C. H. Prescott, Jr., have been very helpful.   Professor Wendell M. Latimer has read the manuscript and offered particularly valuable suggestions and encouragement.   Wally Decker has helped with two drawings.   It is also a pleasure to acknowledge the cooperative spirit of the publishers, Prentice-Hall, Inc.

The photography is the work of Cedric Wright.   Anyone who has tried to photograph glass will realize the difficulties involved, but those who have seen Mr. Wright's thirty-five prints in the Museum of Modern Art will have expected the outstanding job he has done for the book.

For permission to use material in the book, the assistance of the following is acknowledged:

Ace Glass, Inc.; American Chemical Society and Professor G. R. Robertson; Corning Glass Works; Cleveland Welds Works; General Electric Co. and Mr. R. O. Brosemer; Lamp Dept. of the General Electric Co. and Mr. H. D. Blake; General Electric X-Ray Corp.; National Safety Council; Pitman Publishing Co. and Mr. C. J. Phillips; Prentice-Hall, Inc., and Professor John Strong; Reinhold Publishing Corp. and Dr. George W. Morey; Scientific Glass Apparatus Co.; and Stupakoff Ceramic & Mfg. Co.

The author will appreciate the bringing to his attention of any errors, either of omission or commission.

JULIUS D. HELDMAN

Berkeley, California

# Contents

# CONTENTS

# CHAPTER I

## Properties of Glass

GLASSES may be defined as undercooled liquids. The glassy state is not confined to silicates and borates; a great many organic substances—for example, ethyl alcohol and glycerol—can be made to exist below their melting points as glasses. In addition, many mixtures of simple compounds which might be expected to crystallize on cooling, such as *normal* and *iso*-butane, or even the elementary mixture of sulfur and selenium, will form glasses. The best glass formers are "unsymmetrical" molecules with residual forces tending to form bonds between different molecules, for these forces prevent rapid orientation of the molecules into the positions necessary for crystal formation upon cooling.

Glasses are characterized by their lack of macrocrystalline structure and by their rigidity (or high viscosity) relative to the melt. They have no definite melting points, but rather softening ranges. They exhibit both plastic and elastic properties, though the extent of these properties will vary enormously with different glasses and temperatures. They are generally, but not necessarily, transparent. Many glasses, like boric acid, are extremely difficult to devitrify; others spontaneously crystallize more or less rapidly.

**Soft glass and Pyrex.** Before the first World War, the glasses most commonly in use in the scientific laboratories were various makes of "soft" glass, usually known as soda or lime-soda glass. Today in the United States, Pyrex No. 774[1] glass is used practically to the exclusion of other kinds for laboratory and industrial equipment construction, although soft glass is still used in the large-scale commercial production of apparatus. In addition, glasses with special properties are

---

[1] See Glossary, Part A.

available, as is also vitreous silica (commonly but incorrectly called *quartz*).

TABLE 1

SOME PHYSICAL PROPERTIES OF GLASSES[a]

| Glass | Linear Expansion Coefficient[b] $\times 10^7$ | Strain Point,[c] deg. C | Annealing Point,[d] deg. C | Softening Point,[e] deg. C |
|---|---|---|---|---|
| Vitreous silica................ | 5 | 1070 | 1140 | 1650 |
| Vycor, Corning 790.......... | 8 | 790 | 890 | 1510 |
| Pyrex, Corning 774.......... | 32 | 510 | 553 | 819 |
| Nonex, Corning 772.......... | 36 | 494 | 526 | 756 |
| Corning 705AJ.............. | 46 | 461 | 496 | 703 |
| Lead glass, Corning G1....... | 90 | 389 | 425 | 626 |
| Lime glass, Corning G8....... | 92 | 475 | 510 | 696 |

[a] Data from various sources. For references, consult Morey, George W., *Properties of Glass*, Reinhold Publishing Corporation, New York, 1938.

[b] Defined as $(1/l_0)(\Delta l/\Delta t)$ from 0° to 300° C, where $l_0$ is the length at 0° C. The figures represent mean values for the temperature interval. The expansion coefficient of a glass varies considerably with its thermal history. It is fairly constant up to the "transformation temperature" (viscosity from $10^{13}$ to $10^{14}$ poises), where it rises sharply in a short temperature interval (see Morey, pp. 172, 267).

[c] Defined arbitrarily as the temperature at which a glass can be annealed in 16 hr. The viscosity at this temperature, below which flow practically ceases, is $4.0 \times 10^{14}$ poises.

[d] The temperature at which a glass can be annealed in 15 min. The viscosity at this temperature is $2.5 \times 10^{13}$ poises.

[e] Arbitrarily defined in terms of the rate of elongation of a fiber under its own weight. The viscosity at this temperature is $4.7 \times 10^7$ poises.

Soft glasses contain sodium, potassium, calcium, and varying amounts of aluminum and iron, all combined with sand as complex silicates. Iron tends to color the glass green; arsenic, and nowadays selenium, are used in small amounts as decolorizing agents. Addition of lead, usually in place of calcium, gives rise to lead glass, which is much used in decorative tableware. Pyrex No. 774 glass, on the other hand, contains a larger percentage of silica, less of the alkalies, practically no calcium, a substantial amount of boron, and a little aluminum. Nonex No. 772[2] is a low-expansion borosilicate glass containing lead.

[2] See Glossary, Part A.

Soft glass, Pyrex, and all other inorganic glasses are poor heat conductors and, except near their softening ranges, good electrical insulators. This first fact makes it possible to use an extension of glass as a working handle without protecting the hands.

TABLE 2

EXPANSION COEFFICIENTS OF METALS
AND ALLOYS

| Material | Linear Expansion Coefficient[a] $\times 10^7$ |
|---|---|
| Tungsten.............. | 45 |
| Kovar................. | 47[b] |
| Fernico............... | 52[b] |
| Molybdenum.......... | 54 |
| Platinum............. | 89 |
| Copper............... | 166 |
| Dumet................ | ...[c] |

[a] The mean value of $(1/l_0)(\Delta l/\Delta t)$ from 0° to 100° C.

[b] Kovar and Fernico have expansion characteristics like those of glasses, rising rapidly in a short temperature interval (about 450° C).

[c] Dumet, a copper-sheathed iron-nickel alloy, has no well-defined coefficient of expansion. Typical values for 28 B & S gauge wire are $65 \times 10^{-7}$ for the axial coefficient and $95 \times 10^{-7}$ for the radial. See Hull, A. W., and Burger, E. E., *Physics*, **5**, 384 (1934).

**Expansion of glasses.** Table 1 gives a comparison of the coefficients of expansion of some glasses. It should be apparent that only materials with the same or slightly different coefficients of expansion can be successfully sealed at high temperatures without setting up strains on cooling that must of necessity spoil the work. For reference, expansion coefficients of some metals are given in Table 2. Platinum can be successfully sealed to lead glass, but will not make vacuum-tight seals to 774. Tungsten wire up to about 30-mil diameter can be sealed through 774, though such seals are subject to thermal strain; larger pieces of tungsten are first sealed into a

Nonex No. 772 sleeve, which may in turn be welded success-fully to 774. Soft glass-to-Pyrex No. 774 seals always shatter upon cooling. However, by the use of special techniques, many materials of very different expansion coefficients may be successfully sealed. Some of these techniques are treated in Chapter X.

**Thermal behavior.** Silica glass may be heated white hot and then immediately plunged into cold water without crack-ing, for its contraction on cooling is so small that the cohesive strength of the material is great enough to keep the relatively small strains introduced from starting a crack. On the other hand, soft glass heated to a few hundred degrees centigrade will certainly shatter when placed in cold water, or may crack if exposed to a sudden draft, for here the large strains intro-duced upon rapid heating or cooling overcome the cohesive strength of the glass. Pyrex No. 774 lies between soft glass and fused silica in this respect. Tubing up to 15 mm can usually be exposed directly to a gas-oxygen flame without cracking.

Since glass is a poor heat conductor, it is possible to set up large temperature differentials between the outer "skin" and the body of a piece of glass when heating is first started. This temperature difference sets up strains which lead to cracks. The same may also be said of cooling. Here the "skin" cools more quickly than the body.

If a piece of glass is heated at one spot only, without rotation in the flame, similar strains will appear. Although spot heating is definitely necessary for many glass-working operations, it is always a good idea first to heat the whole surrounding area slowly and evenly, starting with a soft yellow flame and continuing with a large brush flame, to the point at which the glass just begins to vaporize sodium—that is, to impart the typical yellow color to the flame. This pre-caution need not be observed with Pyrex No. 774 glass up to about 15 mm on simple manipulations such as making **T** seals.

The proper way to heat a piece of glass evenly is to rotate it uniformly while it is in the flame. After it has been removed from the flame, it must still be rotated, assuming axially symmetrical work is desired. Two factors enter in here: Heat conduction in air is upwards, so that the under side of the glass is cooled and hence solidified while the top is still plastic; and glass undergoes gravitational flow, thus tending to add to the effect of the blow on the bottom side and to subtract from it on the top. In other words, hot glass sags. This fact makes it extremely difficult to blow neat horizontal seals with a hand torch.

**Annealing.** A large or complicated piece of apparatus may be assumed to be strained after it is blown. Sometimes, if complicated but small, it may be set aside to cool without further ado or mishap; but reheating will practically always crack it. The proper procedure is to anneal the glass. Ideally, glass is annealed in a thermostatically controlled oven or a lehr. In these devices, the still-hot glass is placed in a chamber heated to a temperature at which the glass is rigid enough to keep its over-all shape but plastic enough to flow so as to relieve internal strains. It is then cooled slowly and evenly to room temperature. Even though strains must develop on further cooling after the glass "sets," these strains are never great enough to rupture the glass. Table 1 lists the characteristic temperatures for various glasses used in the laboratory.

Most laboratories do not have an annealing oven, and hot glass must be cooled slowly by judicious use of flames. After a piece of work has been blown, it is heated uniformly over a wide area surrounding the work to a temperature just below the softening point but above the strain point. For 774 this corresponds to incipient red heat. Next, the work is rotated uniformly in a large, slightly yellowish brush flame. Finally, a very yellow, sooty flame is used to cover the work evenly with a deposit of lampblack. The work is then set aside, preferably with no hot surface in contact with anything, in a place free from drafts. For complicated soft glass, wrapping the worked parts in cotton is often recommended, but this precaution should never be necessary for 774 unless the room is drafty.

Presumably the lampblack coat serves to give a surface

which tends to cool more slowly and evenly than a clear glass face, though the quantitative extent to which this is true is probably small.   The real reason for specifying the soot layer is to insure even exposure of the worked glass to a soft, cooling flame.

Some glass blowers recommend heating of thin glass in any complicated assembly to a little higher temperature than adjacent thicker glass, for the reason that the thin glass cools more quickly, and hence would then approach annealing conditions at about the same time as the thicker parts.   Such a procedure is practically impossible in many cases, and furthermore it is dangerous because the thin glass is easily heated above its softening point, so that the finished work may be spoiled and may require further treatment.   At best, such a procedure may help a little in relieving strains, but it does not seem reliable enough to justify its use.

**Devitrification.**   Every glass has a characteristic temperature range in which crystals (or at least submicroscopic oriented aggregates) can form and will not redissolve without very intense heating.   In this temperature range glass tends to devitrify.   However, for Pyrex-brand glasses, the rate of devitrification is slow and the temperature range small, so that translucent worked Pyrex is seldom encountered. A translucent or opaque appearance in 774 may usually be cured by heating the glass more strongly and by blowing gently and keeping the two parts of the hot joint absolutely stationary with respect to one another until they cool below red heat.

None of the chemical methods for treating devitrification are infallible.   Sprinkling the hot glass with various salt crystals is often harmful.   Rinsing with aqueous hydrofluoric acid sometimes helps if only surface devitrification is involved.   Indeed, devitrification is seldom encountered with 774, and even when present does not seem to impair the strength of the work.   Cleanliness is the most important factor in combating cloudiness in worked glass.   It should be a general rule not to heat dusty, greasy, or otherwise dirty glass.

# CHAPTER II
## Flames and Torches

**Flame characteristics.** Flames are flowing gases that have become hot enough to luminesce, usually chemically—that is, in which the heat of a chemical reaction has brought the gases to a temperature at which they give off light. The reaction is almost always combustion, the combustible gas (natural gas, producer gas, butane, acetylene, or even hydrogen) being combined with a supply of oxygen from air or the pure gas, and continuously ignited at a given point or area. A "reducing" flame is one in which the combustible gas stream exceeds the equivalent oxygen flow necessary to produce complete combustion of the gas; hence the ignited gas still has hot, unreacted reducing agents in it. Such flames are almost always yellow and are often smoky and sooty with lampblack. Oxidizing flames contain an excess of oxygen; they are usually blue or, in strong daylight, practically colorless. They are necessarily used in working lead glass and Nonex No. 772.

If the velocity of gas issuing from a nozzle exceeds the backward speed of the flame, then the flame will propagate itself away from the nozzle. Such flames are usually unstable and blow out. If, on the other hand, the speed of propagation of the flame is greater, it will "backfire"—that is, the flame will enter the issuing nozzle to the point of mixture of the gases. In general, with stable flames, a steady flow state will be reached in which the flame head will be stationary and close to (but not touching) the nozzle.

By proper engineering of the torch, flames may be made to be "brush" type or "focusing." These aspects will be considered later.

**Heating equipment.** The minimum amount of heating equipment necessary to do Pyrex No. 774 work with tubing up to one inch in diameter is a hand torch, connecting tubing,

7

and a controllable source of gas and oxygen.    The latter two are a *sine qua non*, to which may be added an air supply if soft glass is to be worked.    Available and useful torches are large in number.    After some practice, every worker will develop preferences for certain torches.    Limitations of economy and availability usually determine the amount and type of heating equipment on a glass-working bench, but it is most certainly worth while to have at hand more than one type of burner.

**Bunsen burner.**    The Bunsen burner is the most common laboratory burner.    For pulling, bending, and fire polishing small-bore soft-glass tubing, it is quite satisfactory.    The oxidizing flame is of the focusing type—that is, with a relatively cold inner cone surrounded by a hot, fairly well-defined tapering area.    Such flames are used for heating small areas. When a bend is required, a long surface of glass must be heated, and a fan tip (fishtail) must be slipped over the burner tip.    The resultant flame is still focused but is long and thin.

One important use of the Bunsen burner is as a pilot light. There are times when the blowing out of a blast brush flame would be disastrous; here a pilot proves its value as well as acting as a permanent "match" for the hand torch.

**Meker burner.**    The Meker burner is in essence a number of Bunsen burners in juxtaposition.    When properly adjusted, the oxidizing flame is quite even in temperature distribution. It may be used for bending soft glass or even small 774 tubing.    Two Mekers side by side can be used successfully to bend 774 up to 10- or 11-mm o.d.    The Meker, since it gives a large, even flame, not quite so hot as a gas-oxygen flame, can be used for the initial heating of large glass and also for annealing, though other burners may be more suitable. For slow heating, the reducing flame (air inlets partially shut) is first applied, and the air supply is gradually increased.

**Initial heating.**    Most professional glass blowers use a mammoth multiple-jet or "locomotive" type burner, to which oxygen can also be fed, for initial heating and annealing.    These burners are only a few inches high and may be set in front of another torch to give general, even heating in

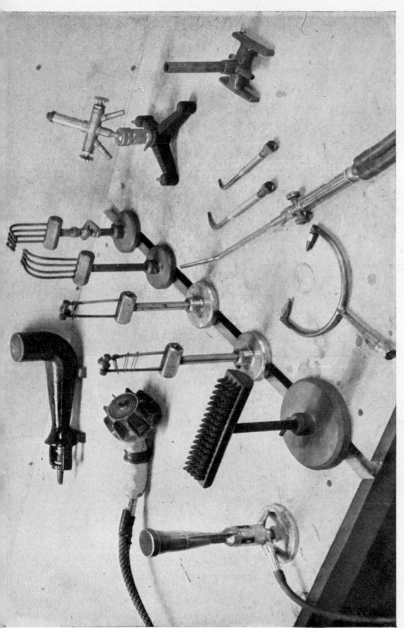

**Fig. 1. Common types of heating equipment.** At the left of the slot in the bench are a Meker-type burner, a "locomotive" with gas and oxygen inlets, and another with gas inlet and air injector. In the slot are a "waffle" or ribbon burner used in bending large tubing and single- and multiple-jet cross-fires. At the right are shown a hand torch with replaceable tips, including cross-fires (splicing torci), a Bunsen burner, and a blast lamp with gas and oxygen taps and two alternative tips stored on the legs.

conjunction with a smaller, hotter flame.   With oxygen, similar burners can be used for working tubing of over two inches.

**Hand torches.**   The simplest torch is a hand torch.   The most common types give focused flames (with oxygen), and a number of alternate tips of different sizes give flames from tiny pinpoints up to about a half inch in diameter.   For use with air (though with 774 air is never used), a multiple-jet tip is usually furnished.

**Permanent torches or blast lamps.**   Permanent torches of the kind most popular on glass-working benches ten years ago have a sliding outer sleeve and two or three alternate tips. They are fitted with gas and oxygen taps and often with a third valve for air.

**Use of the torch.**   The variables that determine the type of flame are the sleeve position and the gas-air-oxygen ratio; the size is largely determined by the tip and gas-flow rate. The use of air leads to a noisy brush flame.   With 774 air is employed only for preheating and annealing and, rarely, for giving stability to a large brush flame.   In practice, it is almost never necessary to use air when working with 774.

In a torch, oxygen (or air) is fed through the inner tube terminating in the nozzle.   In some hand torches, the gases are mixed in the barrel, but generally gas is delivered to the annular orifice between the inner tube and the sleeve.   If the sleeve end is far in front of the nozzle tip, the resultant flame is a long, thin, tapering cone with uneven yellow at the jet base.   Though the burner is often used this way in the laboratory, such a technique is not good for the torch, tending to oxidize and burn the sleeve tip.

The sleeve end should be practically even with or behind the nozzle tip.   If the gas flow is small and the oxygen-gas ratio not too high, a quiet, pointed flame results.   With more oxygen, a hissing, pointed flame starting a few millimeters from the nozzle ensues.   This is a favorite flame of professionals.   It is changed into a noisy brush flame by increasing both gas and oxygen supply.   Now if the oxygen supply on a large brush flame is carefully lowered, a yellow, reducing brush flame may be obtained.

**Cross-fires.** In the past two decades, techniques in glass working have changed enormously. Multiple fires and cross-fires have invaded all but the small laboratories, where they should become standard equipment. Their advantages are

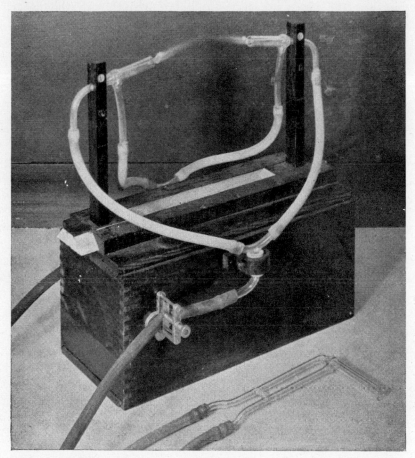

**Fig. 2. Glass torches.** The cross-fires are mounted on a sliding tongue-and-groove base and are shown with screw clamps adjusted to give small, focused flames.

obvious: They provide more uniform and faster heating. Foot-pedal valve controls are desirable with cross-fires. These can be easily made from gas cocks to which are attached steel springs, so that the flow of gas and oxygen is almost, but not quite, shut off when foot pressure is removed from the pedals mounted to the cock handles.   The idling mixture is adjusted to act as a convenient pilot light, so that the fires do not have to be relit every time foot pressure is released. With such an arrangement, work mounted on rollers (see Chapter III) does not have to be removed from the flame area for blowing.   The use of foot pedals practically makes it necessary to work in a sitting position.

**Torches from glass.**   It is not necessary to purchase torches for most work.   Very satisfactory ones may be constructed from glass, as illustrated in Fig. 2.   The outer sleeve is 10-mm o.d.   The inner nozzle tapers to about 1.5-mm i.d. at the tip, which terminates 2 mm from the end of the sleeve. Another variation is to make the outer sleeve of brass, braze on a gas-inlet tube, and insert a glass nozzle through a rubber stopper.   With glass cross-fires, a necessary precaution is to make certain that one fire does not heat the other glass torch.

Valve control with glass heating equipment is obtained by use of small brass needle valves or mounted screw clamps. A lubricated stopcock is permissible as a gas valve, but grease must never be permitted to come in contact with oxygen.   The primary source of oxygen is usually a high-pressure cylinder.   It should be controlled by a reduction valve, set at about 8 lb. pressure, gauge.   Needle valves are unsatisfactory for control of high pressure.[1]

---

[1] Heating equipment when properly used is quite safe, but there are a few precautions to observe.   Bulletin No. 95, "Safe Practices in Handling Compressed Gases," National Safety Council, 20 N. Wacker Drive, Chicago, Ill., is a valuable guide for the glass worker and may be obtained from the Council.

# CHAPTER III

## Equipment

GLASS blowing is like many other arts in that basic work may be done satisfactorily with relatively simple equipment, but special tools have been developed for practically every type of operation. It is the purpose of this chapter to describe glass-blowing equipment, starting with the bare essentials and progressing to the many specialized articles. Practically all the equipment described in this chapter may be obtained from scientific apparatus and supply companies or can be made in the laboratory shop. Torches and accessory equipment have already been discussed (Chapter II).

**First aid; goggles.** Most important on the list is first-aid equipment, for everyone who works with glass must expect at some time to be burned or cut. Didymium goggles are a great help in protecting the eyes, not so much from cuts and burns, which are rare there, but from the intense sodium color of heated glass. Didymium glass (Corning No. 512) contains a mixture of two rare earths, neodymium and praeseodymium, and the combination shows a remarkable selective light absorption in the region of the sodium D line. A 2-mm thickness of didymium glass gives practically complete absorption of the sodium color encountered at the working temperature range for Pyrex. With these glasses, it is also possible to correlate the color temperatures of Pyrex with its working characteristics.

**Stock glass.** A good glass stock is a *de facto* requirement for glass blowing. Soft glass tubing should either be kept away from the laboratory proper or at least kept strictly segregated from Pyrex No. 774 supply. All small odd pieces left after working soft glass should be destroyed at once. Every laboratory will require its own general stock list of 774. Two-mm cane for use as welding rod is a useful item

13

not often encountered, though welding rod may be drawn down from larger cane. Glass tubing and cane should be stored horizontally, if possible, on a solid bottom, since even at room temperature they undergo a slow plastic flow. This fact does not become important unless long pieces of tubing or rod are used. The storage should be kept as free from dust as is feasible. All special glasses should be kept separately and labeled. Calipers or their equivalent are indispensable where glass is used.

**Distinguishing between glasses.** A digression into the ways of distinguishing between soft glass and Pyrex glass would appear to be proper here, for it is one of the problems related to glass storage. The simplest way is to compare the flame behavior of the piece in question with authentic soft glass and Pyrex No. 774 of the same size. Soft glass almost always cracks upon rapid heating (though this is a costly type of trial), becomes workable at a lower temperature, stays workable longer, and usually shows a slight orange luminescence somewhat below color temperatures. A little practice makes it easy to distinguish the two when use of the flame is permissible. The practice of looking down the axis of a tube to judge its character from the color of the walls, soft glass being green in contradistinction to the light yellow of 774, is not recommended, for the color of glasses is very remarkably changed by small amounts of metals such as iron and arsenic.[1]

A unique and foolproof method for determining the type of a suspect glass from only a tiny fragment is as follows: The end of a piece of authentic Pyrex No. 774 cane is heated and flattened; on the flattened end is placed the fragment in question. The spot is reheated strongly without rotation, flattened again, once more heated, and then quickly pulled out to a long thin ribbon. If the suspect glass is Pyrex

---

[1] Pyrex chemical resistant glass No. 774 made before 1935 contained a small amount of arsenic oxide, which imparted a straw-yellow color to tubing viewed down the wall end. With the removal of arsenic oxide from the formula, though the physical properties and heating characteristics are practically identical with the original glass, 774 no longer shows the distinctive end color. "Old" glass may still be *tentatively* identified by color.

No. 774, the ribbon will show no tendency to curl; if it is soft glass, it will spontaneously form a spiral. The technique may be applied to other glasses with very different coefficients of expansion. If a piece of glass is fused to any known type of glass and does not curl, it can be identified as the same general type as the known glass; if it curls, it is a different type. The principle is the same as that in any bi-species expansion element, and it is necessary only to be sure that the two pieces of glass have not lost their identity by flow in the melt.

**Stoppers.** Stoppers for open ends of glass are a necessity. The usual equipment of a laboratory—corks and borers, rubber stoppers, and the like in assorted sizes—are adequate. Many laboratories find it convenient to have a drawer or rack of bored stoppers of all sizes with glass tubing inserted in them for use as a handle or blow end.

**Asbestos.** Asbestos tape and asbestos paper can also be used to stopper open ends that are to be heated. These two items have so many uses in glass blowing that it is advisable to have them at hand if at all possible. The thin asbestos paper can always be substituted for the tape.

**Blow tube, swivel, and mouthpiece.** A length of light rubber tubing should always be kept handy for blowing work that is awkward to bring to the mouth. For rotation of such work, a small swivel, a useful but much neglected adjunct, is employed. If a rubber tube alone is used, the worker may clamp his teeth down on the end, shutting off the work from the air. The end of the rubber should be fitted with a mouthpiece, shaped to the worker's taste and strong enough to withstand the force of clamping of the teeth. An old pipe stem is satisfactory. Unthickened glass tubing is dangerous; professionals often blow bulges in thick-walled capillary tubing for the purpose. A glass mouthpiece is of course fire polished.

**Glass cutters.** For cutting or breaking glass, files are the most generally useful and satisfactory instruments. A 6-in. triangular file is suitable; when the edges become dull, they may be reconditioned to form a very good glass knife by

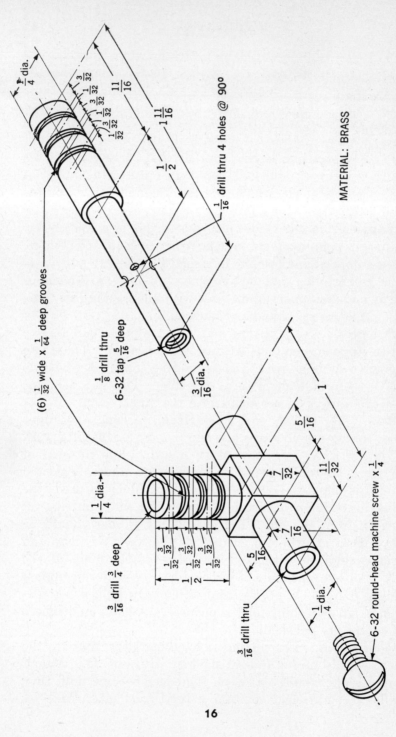

MATERIAL: BRASS

$\frac{1}{4}$ dia.

$\frac{3}{32}$

$\frac{1}{32}$ $\frac{3}{32}$

$\frac{1}{32}$ $\frac{3}{32}$

$\frac{1}{32}$

$\frac{11}{16}$

$1\frac{11}{16}$

$\frac{1}{2}$

$\frac{1}{16}$ drill thru 4 holes @ 90°

(6) $\frac{1}{32}$ wide x $\frac{1}{64}$ deep grooves

$\frac{1}{8}$ drill thru
6-32 tap $\frac{5}{16}$ deep

$\frac{3}{16}$ dia.

$\frac{1}{4}$ dia.

$\frac{3}{16}$ drill $\frac{3}{4}$ deep

$\frac{3}{32}$ $\frac{3}{32}$

$\frac{1}{32}$ $\frac{3}{32}$ $\frac{1}{32}$

$\frac{1}{2}$

$\frac{3}{16}$ drill thru

1

$\frac{5}{16}$

$\frac{11}{32}$

$\frac{7}{32}$

$\frac{7}{16}$

$\frac{5}{16}$

$\frac{1}{4}$ dia.

6-32 round-head machine screw x $\frac{1}{4}$

16

Fig. 3.  Draftsman's isometric sketch of a swivel, showing constructional details.  A less elaborate but quite satisfactory swivel may be made in a machine shop in half an hour.

grinding one face of the triangle smooth. Care should be taken in grinding not to lose the temper of the steel. Flat files are made serviceable by beveling off an edge on a grindstone. Broken unglazed porcelain is an admirable tool for scratching thin-walled capillary such as melting-point tubes.

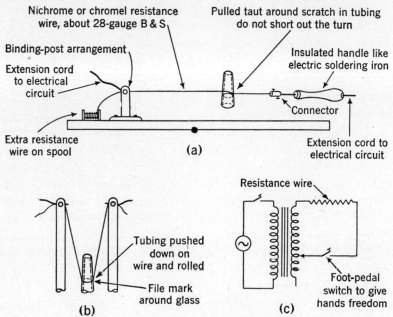

Fig. 4. Hot-wire glass cutters. (a) Loop method. (b) Half loop. (c) Diagrammatic electrical circuit. The variable transformer can be replaced by a rheostat.

Glass knives are in essence like beveled-edge flat files, except that they are made of very hard steel. Tungsten carbide blades are excellent, but they are not to be found in most laboratories. The only necessary tool for breaking glass is a file, since large glass can be severed by the file combined with the use of a piece of rod. A hot-wire appliance, shown in Fig. 4, can be used to advantage, though it is not indispensable. Glass saws are the most elegant tools for cutting tubing and cane, but they are usually beyond the reach of any but professional outlays. A notched thin-metal upright screwed to the side of the bench is useful in breaking short ends.

**Grinding equipment.**  Where grinding is to be done, the equipment should include carborundum powder of different meshes, perhaps 60, 90, 200, 400, and 600 mesh, pumice and rouge, and a supply of flat, thick glass plates.  Power tools for grinding glass are available commercially.

**Carbons.**  Pieces of carbon are very handy on the glass blower's bench.  They are of two types, the first being long dowels with tapered ends, and the second thin rectangular plates or paddles.  Quarter- and half-inch rods, about 10 in. long, are convenient sizes, while the plates should be in the neighborhood of $\frac{1}{2}$ in. by 3 in. by 5 in., preferably with a handle attached.

**Flaring tools.**  Flaring tools are not necessary, since most of their functions can be performed by carbons or a forceps, but they are easy to make.  In their simplest form they are triangular pieces of metal to which handles are attached.  An isosceles triangle of $\frac{1}{8}$- or $\frac{1}{16}$-in. brass or nickel plate, with a $1\frac{1}{2}$-in. base and 2 in. in height, is satisfactory for general use.  Flaring tools with multiple blades can also be used.  Some workers merely file corners on the conical end of a thick carbon rod.

**Forceps; beeswax.**  A pair of long tweezers finds many uses, though small ones become too hot to handle.  Ten- or twelve-in. biological specimen forceps are admirably suited for glass working.  With both flaring tools and forceps, to prevent metal from adhering to the hot glass, it is usually desirable to use beeswax.  Paraffin is a fair substitute.  However, glass that is to be used in high-vacuum apparatus should not be worked with any wax-coated tools.

**Flask holders.**  Professional glass blowers sometimes employ spring jigs or chucks for holding bulbs.  Although they are very handy, it is almost always possible to circumvent their use by temporarily sealing a length of tubing on the base of the flask.

**Rollers.**  In a large professional installation, the two most important items are the lathe or lathes and annealing oven.  Neither will be considered here, for the type of work they handle is certainly beyond the range of this book.

However, an embryonic form of lathe, consisting of mounted metal rollers, can be of great help, especially when large or long glass is encountered. One often sees two rollers on a bench, but rarely the four that are required to handle two large pieces. V-shaped grooves cut in half-inch lumber, padded with asbestos and adjustable in height, can be substituted for rollers.

Nowadays stopcocks and ground joints can be obtained commercially in practically any size and style. Other glassware such as flasks, and metals like platinum and tungsten are a necessary part of a glass blower's equipment. Diverse items such as copper-774 tubing seals and graded seals (774-to-silica, and so forth) can be obtained ready made.

**The glass blower's bench.** The physical outlay of the glass bench is partially a matter of taste if all the resources desired are available, but usually the exigencies of space and supplies determine the character of the work bench. The table is preferably situated so that no strong light shines on the worker. An important consideration is the ventilation—not so much that the room be air-conditioned but that it be draft-free. Ideally, gas, air, and oxygen are piped to the bench; actually, this is seldom so. Gas is usually piped (though a tank of butane and a reduction valve do very nicely), but oxygen is generally stored by the side of the bench in cylinders. For working Pyrex no air supply is needed, but it can be used to advantage, especially on the three-inlet type of torch.

A few suggestions as to the type of bench are appended, though none fall in the necessary category. The working space should be as long as possible. The best covering is transite. Asbestos paper, masonite, and soapstone are usable; wood and paint should be avoided. At the sides and rear, a notched upright border of wood is useful for resting hot glass so that it can cool without direct contact with the bench. Any type of rest is satisfactory.

Most laboratory benches are a little low for glass blowing. The majority of glass blowers, if they stand, would like a bench about 4 ft. high. For working in a sitting position, a

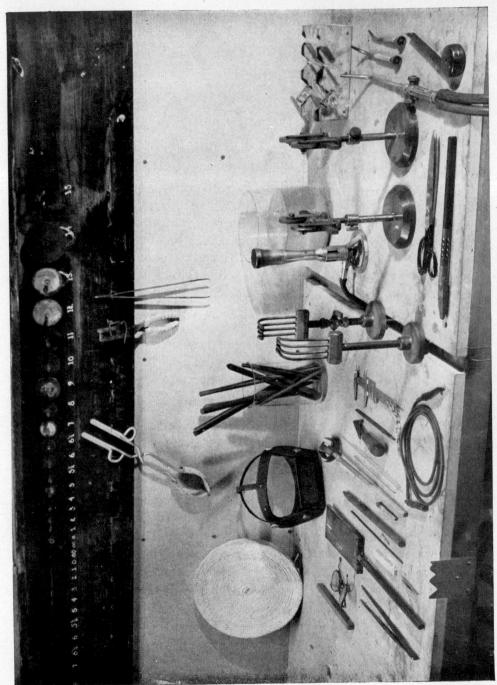

Fig. 5.   Equipment often found on glass-working benches.

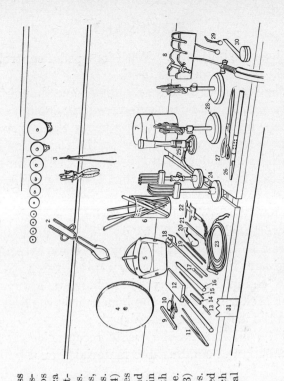

Key: (1) Assortment of rubber stoppers with short glass tubes inserted in the holes. (2) Hot-glass holder with asbestos-covered jaws. (3) Specimen forceps. (4) Roll of asbestos tape. (5) Face and eye protector used in working with silica glass. (6) Carbon rods. (7) Bowl of water, used for shattering hot glass. (8) Small rack for supporting hot glass. (9) Banker's specie sealing wax. (10) Didymium goggles, remounted in a light frame. (11) Another specimen forceps. (12) Carbon paddle with handle. (13) Small tweezers. (14) Unfired soapstone, used in marking glass. The mark it leaves does not "burn" when the glass is subsequently heated, and may be easily wiped off. (15, 16) Carbon rods. (17) Pin vise for holding wires. (18) Small flask holder, made with phosphor-bronze. (19) Welding rod, 2-, 3-, and 5-mm cane. (20) Flaring tool. (21) Triangular file. (22) Calipers. (23) Swivel, hose, and mouthpiece. (24) Multiple cross-fires. (25) Meker burner. (26) Small carbon paddle, also used as a reamer. (27) Scissors. (28) Rollers. (29) Hand torch and tips. (30) Flexible metal rule. (31) Notched metal upright used in breaking small glass.

The bench top is made of half-inch transite sheet.

high stool can be obtained.   With foot-pedal control, a some-what lower bench should be used.

The placing of the torches requires some thought.   A stationary burner should be mounted securely enough so that the valves may be operated without using the other hand to steady the burner, and the hoses to the torch should be led from behind and underneath the bench.   Oftentimes it pays to bore holes in the bench so that the hose connections do not extend over the front.   With foot-pedal control, the bench is slotted and the tubing brought through the slot.

Two worth-while things to do for a hand torch are to devise a rest so that it can be hung up, leads attached, when not in use and, if it is used as an in-place torch, to set up a mount to clamp it.   Many glass blowers always keep a Bunsen or Meker burner on the bench; it is the first flame to be lit and the last to be extinguished.

A not trivial item is the waste receptacle.   It must be made of metal, and combustible material should be kept out.

# CHAPTER IV

## Basic Operations

A SURPRISING number of hot-glass manipulations do not involve blowing, such as cutting, rotation, fire polishing, flaring, "squaring," bending, "pulling a point," shrinking, flanging, and bulging. Since in any glass work the glass must be cut, the various methods of severing glass will be treated first in some detail.

**Cutting glass.** Glass up to 12 or 15 mm in diameter may be severed easily by scratching with a file and then manually breaking at the scratch. The file should be sharp enough so that its "bite" is heard. One or two short strokes are sufficient, since the object is not to grind away so much glass that it is thin at the scratch but rather to start a tiny transverse crack that grows when torque is applied. One method is to press on one flat of a triangular file with a thumb, holding the glass steady with the other hand and resting the glass below the scratch on the forefinger of the file hand. However, even though this procedure gives very sharp cracks, it is hard on thumbs when the glass shatters. It is always advisable to protect oneself either by wrapping the hand in cheesecloth or resting the glass on a flat surface and holding the file back, away from the glass.

After scratching, the glass is grasped in the hands, thumbs adjacent, one on each side of the scratch, and all turned toward the chest. As a precaution to insure against too much leverage, some workers hold the tube very close to the chest, elbows out. Also, with fairly large glass, or with one end rather short, it is advisable to cover the glass with a rag.

The tube is then *pulled* with both hands opposing. In the majority of cases, without any conscious torque applied, the tube will break clean at the scratch. If it does not break, the pull is released and now is reapplied with the addition of a slight bending out of both elbows.  If the glass does not break under these conditions, it should be re-scratched; if it is still recalcitrant, it is probably too large to be broken by this technique, and another method should be tried.  Some glass blowers maintain that wetting the scratch facilitates cracking.  Though the reason is not understood, this is apparently true and is substantiated by some controlled experiments.[1]

If the scratch is too near one end of the tube to be handled with both hands, the side of the tube opposite the scratch is set on a table edge or notched metal upright (the scratch faces the worker) with the small end supported.  This small end is then rapped sharply with the file.  In this case, a deep file scratch is advisable.

A glass knife or a diamond cutter is used in the same way as a file for scratching glass.  Both make thinner marks.

**Cutting with hot cane.**  When the tube is too wide to be broken by the methods discussed above, it is evenly marked with a file around its circumference.  The tip of a thin piece of cane is then heated very hot and at once applied anywhere on the scratch.  If the glass does not crack, the cane is reheated, reapplied, and a drop of water immediately placed at the point of application.  Some technicians prefer to wet the scratch mark before jamming on the cane tip.

**"Leading a crack."**  For very large glass, when one application of the hot rod does not suffice to sever the whole circumference of the tube, the crack is "led" around by placing the hot cane each time beyond the end of the crack and using water if necessary.

**The hot-wire method.**  The hot-wire technique also works well on large glass.  A loop of nichrome or chromel wire, 13 mil (28 gauge B & S), is conveniently led through insulated handles to an adjustable power supply sufficient to heat the loop to red heat (see Fig. 4).  The wire is then wrapped around the circular scratch and held taut, the current is applied for about 30 sec., and water is dripped on the scratch,

[1] See Morey, George W., *Properties of Glass*, p. 323.  Reinhold Publishing Corporation, New York, 1938.

which should then crack clean. Care should be taken not to short the current at the ends of the loop.

**Cutting by blowing out.** In addition to these standard methods of obtaining a given length of glass, one can always heat the glass, seal it, heat it evenly about the circumference, and blow it out. This method is usually neglected in books on glass working; it deserves more attention, since there is far less possibility of a jagged or uneven end resulting after fire polishing.

**Rotation.** In every case where axially symmetrical work is desirable, rotation of the glass in the flame is necessary. Glass tubing is always rotated while soft, even when it is being blown. With one piece, when only the tip is heated, no difficulty arises. Any method of setting up the work (such as with rollers) or holding it will do as long as rotation continues. With heavy pieces, it is possible to bear the work in one hand while rotating with the other. Rotation should not stop until after the glass "sets."

**Simultaneous rotation with both hands.** If the operation is one in which two parts of cool glass are linked by hot, flowing glass, such as in making bends or sealing two tubes lengthwise, it is necessary that both parts be rotated evenly with the same angular velocity. This is the most important single rule in glass blowing.

Two or three methods may be used to accomplish this end. If it is assumed that the worker is right-handed, the most common is for the glass in the right hand to be held between the thumb and first one or two fingers, with the palm, thumb, and fingers pointed up. Sometimes the place at which the fingers join the palm is used as a bearing. The glass can be rotated between the thumb and forefinger about one-quarter to one-eighth turn depending on its size; then, while the glass rests in the fingers-hand crotch, a new grip is taken with the thumb and first finger and another turn accomplished. The prime reason for holding glass in the right hand in this manner is to make it convenient to bring it to the mouth for blowing.

The left hand grips the other end of the glass from above,

with the palm pointed down and the fingers curled. The glass is borne by the tips of the last two or three fingers pressing the tube against the palm; rotation is accomplished by the thumb and forefinger.

One method not generally approved but capable of giving good results is that of gripping the glass with both hands and rotating as described for the left hand above. Actually this method gives good results only after the worker trains himself to flip his right hand under the glass (so that it can be brought to the mouth for blowing) without altering the axial alignment or relative rotation rates of the two ends.

Other methods of rotation have been suggested but are not in common use. These methods include holding the ends of glass like a pen, and so forth. If a roller is used for a bearing, the foregoing methods of rotation still apply; if two rollers support one piece, it may be rolled by the flat hand passing over it.

Having decided which method of rotation to employ, a beginner must then become proficient in it. There is no substitute for practice. Two pieces of glass joined by a thin rubber tube form a good practice tool.

While the two ends of glass are rigidly connected, as in cool tubing that is to be bent, no problem arises in rotation. When the heated area begins to soften, the tubes must finally be aligned axially, without twist, and evenly heated. Some instructors in glass blowing recommend rotating one end at a time, the other being held stationary. Such a technique does work, and well, but the objection is that with small work which is heated quickly, not enough rotation is accomplished to heat the area evenly around the circumference. Of course the temperature of the flame can be decreased, though this may not be desirable with pinpoint flames, since parts adjacent to the weld would reach a relatively higher temperature in the longer heating interval. One satisfactory method is to rotate both ends about one-fourth turn, recover, and rotate again. With practice, the operations are automatic, the time for complete rotation being from 1 to 2 sec.

Some workers hold the work palm under in both hands and roll the glass back and forth in the hand between the thumb and forefinger. A little thought will show that the periphery of a piece of glass is not heated uniformly by such a procedure. However, it is possible to become so proficient with this technique, by varying the angular speed at different parts of the turn, that good even heating results. The left hand is usually finally flipped over the glass for ease in bringing the right-hand end to the mouth for blowing. The only ultimate objection to this technique is that it breaks down for large tubing, with which a complete rotation cannot be accomplished by rolling between thumb and forefinger.

**Fire polishing.** Perhaps the easiest exercise in glass working—and even here rotation is necessary—is fire polishing. A broken end of tubing is brought to the flame and heated until the sharp corners are glazed over. For small glass, no preheating is necessary. Soft glass can be polished in a Bunsen or Meker flame, but only small 774 tubing can be handled in a Meker. It is preferable to use a fairly small sharp flame for the polishing, lest too long an area be heated and the glass sag in.

**Flaring.** If the tip of a tube is heated too strongly and therefore shrinks too far, it can be flared out and thickened (sometimes known as "bordered") by inserting a carbon rod or flaring tool while the glass is still hot, and rolling the glass around while the tool is held steady. To prevent the hot glass from sticking to the metal of the flaring arrow, the tool is first warmed and pressed to a cake of beeswax or paraffin (except in cases in which the glass is to be used in vacuum apparatus). Sometimes the ends of a pair of forceps can be inserted into the shrunken orifice, which is then widened easily by rotation. A common error in flaring is heating too much glass. When the tube is inserted and the tubing rotated, the glass twists rather than flares out.

Glass ends may also be flared by rotating them in the flame while a carbon rod, held at the correct angle, is in the tubing. The carbon should never reach more than a dull red heat, and should be long enough so that it is cool at the gripped end.

Here again only a small length of glass at the tip is heated. By judicious use of this technique, it is possible to make a funnel end on tubing. Before the advent of standard taper

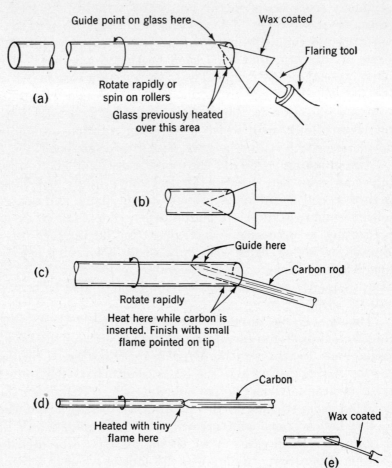

**Fig. 6. Flaring.** (a) Wide flare. (b) Narrower flare, harder to do well because tool has no guide. (c) Flaring and thickening (bordering) with a carbon. (d) Flaring small tubing. (e) With tungsten wire (or file tang).

joints, technicians made their own tapers in this manner and ground them. To prevent the glass from twisting over a long taper, the glass is worked at a low temperature. Flared ends should be rotated as rapidly as possible while being worked, preferably being spun on rollers for neat work.

Fire polished and flared ends, if made with rotation technique, need not be annealed unless they are quite large.

**"Squaring off."** Often the broken end of a piece of glass is not "square." It may be smoothed off by heating the whole end and then spot heating the high places and pulling off the excess glass with a forceps or preferably a piece of 5- or 7-mm cane. The tip of the cane should be hot enough so that red-hot glass will stick to it but not hot enough to be plastic. If only one or two low spots are present, the tubing end is heated evenly, and then a dot of glass is welded onto the low spot from a piece of 2-mm cane. If the weld is thick, it can be heated, squeezed thin with a wax-coated forceps, the excess drawn off, and finally the whole tip thickened and flared evenly as desired.

It is sometimes possible to chip down an uneven, unpolished end of tubing by using a rusted wire gauze. The only objection is that small particles of iron oxide are later fused into the glass, although these usually offer no trouble. There is the slight possibility of a pinhole leak arising from this action.

**Bending.** Small tubing can be bent without blowing. It is of prime importance to rotate it evenly and to heat it over a surface at least seven or eight times its diameter to achieve a good right-angle bend without blowing. If too small an area is heated, the inside of the turn will buckle and the outside will be thin and flattened. Tubing up to 12-mm o.d. can be bent to a right angle without blowing. A very wide, fairly cool flame is best. The author used two Meker burners side by side to bend 12-mm o.d. Pyrex No. 774 into the loop on the tipping McLeod gauge in the frontispiece without blowing. In such a case, a turn of only about 30° can be accomplished at one heating. Rotation for heating the next section is difficult, but in the slow-heating Meker flame it is possible successively to expose different parts of the circumference to the flame for a long enough time to get an even heating. It is a common error to try to bend glass at too low a temperature. Pyrex No. 774 tubing should reach dull

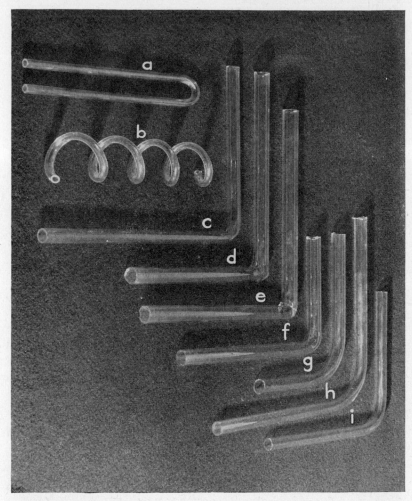

**Fig. 7. Types of bends.**  (a) U-bend, 6-mm tubing.  (b) Mandrel-wound spiral, 6-mm tubing.  Note that the tubing is slightly flattened.  (c) Bad bend, 10-mm tubing.  The outside is flattened, and the inside buckled because too small an area was heated.  (d) Bend made like a T-seal, 12-mm tubing.  (e) Bend made by cutting two tube ends at 45° and sealing, 12-mm tubing.  (f) Bend made by shrinking a small portion of tubing, bending, and blowing out to shape in one puff, 11-mm tubing.  (g, h) Bend made with one Meker burner, bending only 10° to 20° at a time.  (i) Bend made with two Meker burners side by side, one bend.  Note that the radius is smaller than in (g) and (h) and that the tubing is slightly flattened.

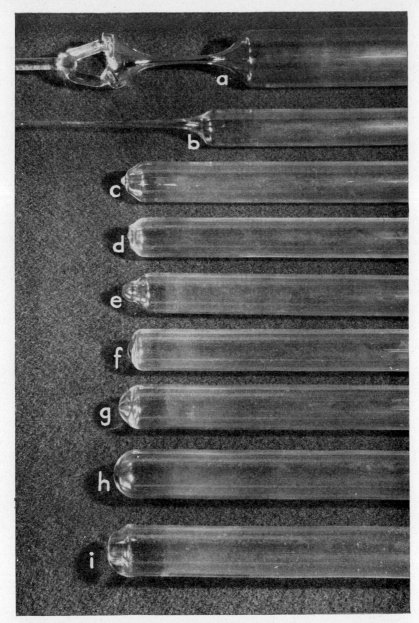

**Fig. 8. The "point" and test-tube end.** (a) A short point on 25-mm tubing, showing how a temporary cane handle is made. (b) A bad point, both axially unsymmetrical and too thin, 16-mm tubing. (c) Excess glass pulled off from a good point. Note the symmetry. (d) Like (c) except that the point was too thin and the tip was shrunk in. (e) Auxiliary bulb blown from end like (c). (f) End heated so that it has flattened. (g) End heated to thick-walled cone. (h) Finished end resulting from blowing on heated end like (f). (i) Thick-walled, unsymmetrical, oversized end, usually resulting from heating as in (g).

red heat.    Also, it is often helpful to pull very slightly while bending.

Beginners are often required to make the fittings for a wash bottle in a Bunsen burner without being supplied with a fan-tip attachment.    The results are never neat.    While a good glass blower can evenly heat quite a length of tubing in a small flame by passing the tubing back and forth as well as rotating it, this is certainly too much to expect of a beginner.

**Nozzles; "pulling a point."**    A nozzle is made by heating a long section of tubing quite hot and "pulling a point" while still rotating.    For a thick-walled, tapered nozzle, the glass over the heated area should be fairly well shrunk before being pulled.    For a shorter nozzle, a smaller area is heated, but just as hot.    Pulling the point before the glass is hot enough results in a thin-walled, fragile nozzle.    Here the effects of uneven rotation show up quite markedly, the nozzle being axially unsymmetrical (see Fig. 8).

The drawn-down part is scratched where desired and cracked.    For scratching thin capillary glass, broken ends of unglazed porcelain are better than a file.    If the nozzle tip is square, it need not be fire polished.

An alternate method of making a nozzle, now preferred by many analysts, is to shrink the tip of 7-mm tubing down to any orifice desired.

**Flanging.**    In making a dropper, the nozzle end is made, and the tubing is cracked off where desired and flared.    Some workers prefer to have a right-angle flange.    Such a flange is made by heating just the tip of a flared end with a pointed flame (the hissing flame does nicely) and pressing a carbon plate against it.    The tip may also be flanged by pressing it against a clean transite board.

An obvious application of squaring, flaring, and flanging glass tubing is in the common job of repairing broken buret tops.    It should be pointed out that most burets are made of soft glass, and care should be taken to heat them very slowly, though a lengthy annealing should not be necessary. A drafty room should be avoided, and the hot part of the glass should not rest on anything while cooling.

**Bomb tubes; temporary handles of cane.** In organic reactions, it is often necessary to prepare bomb tubes. These tubes should be of thick-walled Pyrex. For sealing of the end after the reactants are introduced, a few hints may be of value. Obviously the tube is held almost upright, so that no reactants come near hot glass. If a permanent torch is used, the tip is heated slowly and a handle of cane attached on the circumference of the tip by heating the cane end and other spot strongly and welding them together. Even rotation is admittedly hard with such a handle. If an evenly drawn-down end is necessary, a more elaborate symmetrical handle of cane sealed in two spots to the tip can be made, as shown in Fig. 8.

The whole is then rotated (being held almost perpendicular, of course) in successively hotter flames about an inch below the tip until the heated area is quite soft and has thickened somewhat. It is then pulled, while rotating in the flame, until there is only a few millimeters clearance between the inner walls. Now the area *below* the pull is heated, though not to the softening point; and finally a sharp flame applied at the narrow spot, with pulling, suffices to seal the bomb. The closure must not be reheated to the softening point but should be cooled slowly in a smoky flame. If the job is done properly, very little strain should result. The reason for heating below the constriction before the final seal is to have a volume of hot gas cooling while the final seal is made so that the greater pressure on the outside will tend to push the hot glass together rather than blowing it out.

**The hand torch.** If the bomb tube is immersed in a cooling bath, the hand torch is used. The bomb should be clamped in place. Playing the torch around the periphery of the bomb takes the place of rotation of the tube. If dry ice is used as the refrigerant, it should be used in conjunction with a noninflammable liquid, such as trichlorethylene or chloroform, or one with a high flash point, such as one of the cellosolves, rather than acetone, which has a very low flash point.

**Melting-point tubes.**   Good melting-point tubes are often
a bugaboo to the organic chemist.   They should have very
thin walls for rapid heat transfer.   To achieve this it is
necessary to choose fairly wide diameter tubing to start
with; an ordinary 6-in. test tube, either soft glass or Pyrex,
is satisfactory.   First the closed end is heated and welded
to a cane handle (laboratory stirring rods are almost always
made of soft glass).   Then, with a wide brush flame, a wide
area starting about half an inch from the closed end is heated
until it is soft and beginning to shrink.   The glass is removed
from the flame and is at once pulled as far as it will go; it is
even desirable to have a helper walk away with the handle
end.   The thin-walled capillary is sealed by momentary
exposure to a pinpoint flame in lengths of about 10 cm.   This
procedure keeps the tubes clean and free from dust.   When
needed, the sealed capillaries are scratched with porcelain
in the middle and cracked, giving two melting-point tubes.
If soft glass is used at a bench at which 774 is worked, all
soft glass ends are destroyed or stored well away from the
774 stock.

**Bulges.**   Small glass ends that are to be attached to
rubber tubing are often bulged or nippled (these bulges are
known to some glass blowers as "Marías").   If the glass
tubing has not yet been put on an apparatus, it is convenient
to bulge in the middle of a longer piece, draw down slightly
on the side to be discarded, cool, scratch with a file on the
slight constriction, and then seal on the apparatus.   The
handle is cracked off and fire polished when convenient.
The bulge is made by heating, with rotation, in a pinpoint
flame and gently pushing the two ends together.   Care
must be taken to work the glass at a low temperature.   On
tubing over 12-mm o.d., it may be necessary to blow slightly.

**Temporary tubing handles.**   If the glass end is already
sealed into an apparatus, a temporary handle is employed.
The technique involved, though fairly delicate, is often a valuable aid in working with short ends.   A convenient length
of glass of the same size as the glass to be bulged is selected,
and both tips are heated just above the softening temperature.

For 774 this is a very dull red.  The ends are then placed together, pushed slightly, and held until the temporary weld sets.  Such a joint has enough stability to withstand the usual torques put on it during subsequent work (though it should never support a heavy piece) and can be severed quite cleanly by a sharp rap or jar.   It is important to get both ends of the glass hot enough to stick but not so hot that they flow together.

The bulge is then put on by carefully heating with the pin-point flame about $\frac{3}{8}$ in. from the temporary weld and pushing. Although it may be impossible to rotate the work properly for the bulge, it is always feasible to spot heat about the cir-cumference fairly evenly.   Finally the handle is tapped off, and the end is repolished if necessary.   If the temporary weld is heated to red heat after it is made, the joint may undergo sufficient flow to resist subsequent cracking.

**Blue glass as a practice aid.**   Even rotation and heating have been stressed throughout this chapter as the prime fac-tors in glass work.   As a visual practice aid, the use of blue glass tubing is recommended.   This glass undergoes far more striking visual color changes with temperature, even below the softening point, than do colorless glasses, and one can easily see the relative temperature distribution over all of a heated area.

# CHAPTER V

## Blowing Involving One Piece of Glass

**Sealing a tube end.** One of the most common operations in glass working is sealing off a tube end. From both esthetic and structural standpoints, it is desirable that the sealed end approach in appearance a smooth hemispheroidal surface— a test-tube end. With free 7- or 8-mm tubing, such an aim is easy to achieve. As long as the sealed end is not too thick, is rotated evenly, and is puffed on gently while still being rotated, a good appearance results. With larger tubing, more extended manipulation is necessary.

Two cases are to be considered. The first is a situation in which a long enough piece of tubing is available so that it may be rotated with both hands while being drawn down. In the second, the seal is to be made quite close to the end of the tube. In either event, "pulling a point" is the usual starting operation.

To do this in the first case, the tube is heated until it begins to thicken. For the final heating, the diameter of the flame is one to two times that of the tube. When the glass is hot enough, it is withdrawn from the flame and pulled, both ends being rotated meanwhile. The constriction of the pulled point should be concentric with the two ends, and its extent is judged from the thickness of the main tubing from which the end is to be blown. Large variations in personal preference are permissible in this operation, some workers pulling a long point and others shrinking a rather narrow, thick collar of glass and pulling very little.

In the second case, the end of the glass is heated strongly, and the glass is "gathered" with cane to form a temporary handle coaxial with the tube. Then the tube can be heated and the point pulled. An alternative method is to heat the desired area quite hot while rotating, grasp the hot end by pinching it shut with the forceps, and pull away while continuing to hold the rotating hot glass in the flame and the forceps steady. This procedure gives a twisted point, which is not too desirable but does no great harm if the end is properly worked subsequently. It is desirable to have the tapered part of the same thickness as the main tube. Only experience will tell just how much to thicken the heated walls and how fast to pull to achieve uniform wall thickness.

After the point is pulled, the excess thin tubing is drawn off in a small flame, so that the tube end is sealed. This may be done in the same operation as drawing down the tube. In any event, a little lump of glass will remain at the tip. Some of this excess glass can be pulled off after it is heated in a pin-point flame. However, it cannot all be removed this way. If the lump is not too large, the best way to handle the situation is to heat this lump in a small flame and blow it out into an auxiliary bulb.

**Blowing.** In blowing glass, one uses his cheeks and gives a succession of gentle puffs rather than one continuous blow from the lungs, since control rather than excessive pressure is desired. With large pieces of Pyrex that will remain workable for some time, and with all soft glass, it is necessary to rotate while blowing to counteract the effects of gravity and uneven cooling of the hot glass. This does not and cannot mean that a steady rotation is kept up while the glass is in the mouth, although it is possible if a swivel rubber hose and mouthpiece are used. Rather the glass is held, puffed on, turned, again blown, and so on until the desired shape is reached or the glass has set. It is often advantageous to blow glass in such a position that the hot portion is axially vertical. With a tube end this means that the end points either up or down. Specific effects can be achieved by these actions.

After the auxiliary bulb has been blown, the burner is changed to give a brush flame of about the same diameter as the tube, and the whole end is heated. If the auxiliary bulb is not too thin, it will shrink uniformly without collapsing, so that the whole end assumes a flat or conical appearance. This end is then blown out to shape.

From this point on, it is difficult to apply any set rules.

Probably the most common troubles encountered are irregular thickness of glass, off-center end, and lumpy tip.  The first and second can be cured in theory by heating the glass long enough with perfectly even rotation, since the surface tension of the hot glass tends to make it flow evenly over the rounded end.  In practice, however, extended working often makes the end more off center than ever; the bulgy part is usually thinner and hence reaches a higher temperature in the flame and blows out farther.  It would be nice if all test-tube ends were axially aligned, but unfortunately it is often necessary to heat only one part of the end to doctor the job, and spot heating is never completely satisfactory.  This heating should never be applied to a small spot, but to a substantial section of the end, say a quarter or half of the periphery.  The glass is then blown, and general heating is not resumed until the hotter spot has had a chance to cool a little.

A lumpy tip is always worked out by applying a pinpoint or hissing flame to the lump and blowing a small auxiliary bulb, which is then heated and shrunk along with the rest of the end in the brush flame.  A small symmetrical lump on the end actually does no harm.

If the end appears too flat, it may be turned down for blowing.  This operation tends to make the side walls a little thinner.  With a long end, the tip is turned up to thicken and shorten it.  Here very even rotation is necessary to prevent the hot glass from tipping to one side.

Very often it will be found that the end has a little larger diameter than the tube; that is, a small bulb has been blown.  If this bulb does no harm it may be left; if necessary, the glass starting at the bulge is drawn down and a new end blown.

Large or long glass can be handled in a roller, using a swivel, a rubber tube, and a mouthpiece.  Such work can be rotated horizontally while being blown, theoretically the most ideal situation.  In situations in which even rotation is not possible, the end should be played in a large, fairly cool flame so as to heat the whole area evenly.

**Vial end.**  To make a flat bottom, the test-tube end is reheated in a fairly small flame, with rotation, until the end has more or less flattened out because of surface tension. The glass is then removed from the flame and pressed against a carbon paddle or transite board. This procedure usually results in a bottom with a very slight inverted cone. To get a flat bottom, the tube is gently blown on while the end is in contact with the hot surface.

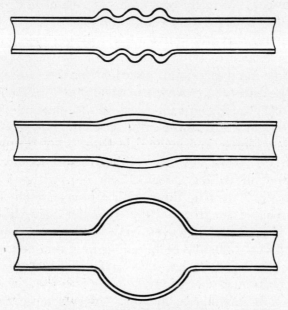

Fig. 9. Blowing a bulb in the middle of a tube.

**Bulb end.** Blowing a bulb on the end of a tube is merely an extension of blowing a test-tube end. It is necessary only to gather more glass and heat a larger area. The bulb must never be blown out so that a very thin section results, for this section will buckle, often irreparably, on further heating. It should never be necessary to blow a bulb of more than twice the diameter of the original tubing with Pyrex No. 774. For bulbs of larger size it is more efficient and safer to seal on a piece of tubing of the desired diameter or, for very large bulbs, to seal to the apparatus a round-bottomed flask.

**Bulb in the middle of a tube.** For blowing a bulb in the middle of a tube, glass is gathered at ¼- to ½-in. intervals by heating with a small flame and pushing together, with slight blowing if necessary to keep the inner diameter from decreasing.] Two or three such bulges are sufficient. Then a large brush flame is applied to the whole area, which is rotated until a thick, smooth wall results. The inner diameter should not be allowed to shrink, but it is always blown out slightly when necessary. The final heating should be done in a wide but fairly cool flame, since a wide mass of very fluid glass is almost impossible to handle.

The above may sound like a fairly simple task, but in practice blowing an *even* bulb in the middle of a tube is one of the hardest free-hand glass manipulations for the average worker, especially with 774. Anyone who can consistently blow esthetically pleasing and mechanically strong bulbs in 15-mm tubing is ready for the most extended manipulations in laboratory glass working.

**Bends.** It is almost impossible to make a smooth right-angle bend in tubing over 12-mm o.d. without blowing. Theoretically it can be done with a long enough flame, the ratio of heated length to tube diameter being the critical factor. Practically, however, both the lack of proper equipment and the difficulty of handling long sections of flowing glass usually make it desirable to finish bends by blowing. For the beginning operation the glass is heated in as wide a flame as it is possible to muster. After some practice, one can effectively widen the flame by passing the glass back and forth over it as well as rotating it. When a wide area is evenly hot, it is bent, with slight blowing and pulling, making sure that the outside of the bend has not flattened nor the inside buckled. With glass up to 12 or 15 mm a large brush flame should make it possible to finish the **L** with one manipulation. If the bend is not yet perpendicular, it should be reheated not at the old bend center but to one side. Now even rotation is impossible but may be approximated with a wide, fairly cool flame.

After the bend is made, it should be smoothed if necessary with a flame about the diameter of the tube. Usually the major kinks are on the inside of the bend. These spots are heated until the kink and the area surrounding it are evenly red and then puffed gently into shape. Spot heating with a pinpoint flame in any operation leads to a "hammered-bronze" finish, which may be serviceable with small glass but which is never so desirable as a smooth surface.

Sharper bends may be made by sealing two separate pieces of glass at the proper angle (Chapter VI), or by a method often used by accomplished technicians but requiring good control of hot glass. In this method, the tube, with one end stoppered or sealed for blowing, is heated with rotation in a hot, wide flame until a length equal to about two diameters is sagging hot and has shrunk to half its initial diameter. The glass is removed from the flame, bent, and then rapidly blown out to initial size or slightly larger. If the glass is hot enough, the bend will not buckle on the inner side or flatten on the outer. These techniques are illustrated in Fig. 7.

**Healing cracks.** The healing of cracks in small tubing is fairly simple. On small 774 tubing not involving triple (or ring) seals or lumpy glass, the glass is heated, carefully at first (a Bunsen or Meker burner makes a good starting point), and finally with a hot flame. Many cracks will heal spontaneously. It is then necessary only to blow lightly to give the shrunken hot spot its initial shape, or, if it is near an open end, to ream it out with a carbon rod. If the edges pull away, leaving a small orifice, welding rod is added until the opening is sealed, and the spot is blown as smooth as possible. The work is cooled slowly. In using welding rod, it is advisable to add as small an amount as possible; for this reason 1- or 2-mm rod is preferable. Rod of this size can always be drawn down from a larger cane.

The procedure for healing cracks in large tubing, beakers, and the like differs mainly in the initial heating, which should be very slow and diffuse. It is often advisable to heat about an inch away from the ends of the crack first, so that if the crack grows when intense heat is applied, it will stop at the hot glass on the edges.

Healing a crack in large soft glass is an almost hopeless task. It might be reiterated that, though Pyrex equipment may seem more expensive, it is actually cheaper when its greater mechanical strength, heat-shock resistance, and reparability are compared with those of soft glasses.

# CHAPTER VI
## End and T Seals

**End seals. Both tubes of same diameter.** The operations involved in making tubular end-to-end seals with both glass tubes of the same diameter are in the main shown in Fig. 10. The importance of this fundamental manipulation cannot be overemphasized; hence, in addition to the photographic examples, some of the details are explained in the following discussion.

The tube ends should be squared before starting. Any imperfections in the tube ends will show up as lumps or thin spots in the final join unless it is subjected to prolonged working in the flame. Some glass blowers prefer to flare and thicken the ends before starting; this procedure is not necessary with small tubing, though with glass over 1 in. in diameter flaring may facilitate the initial seal.

Personal preference and experience determine the flame size. After the preheating with a wide, soft flame, a good working flame is between radius and diameter size. For finishing the joint smooth, a flame twice as wide and somewhat cooler is used.

**Rotation method.** The two ends are simultaneously heated with rotation (the tip of one piece being closed for blowing) until the glass at the tips has begun to shrink. The ends are then removed from the flame, brought together, pressed slightly, and blown rather hard with perhaps a little pull. It is extremely important that the ends be brought together squarely. Some workers bring the ends together at an angle so that only a small part of each touches; then the rest is guided into place by decreasing the angle. If the two pieces do not seal securely, leaving a hole, it is best to reheat the whole joint with slight pressing.

It is not absolutely necessary that the glass be removed from the flame for joining. Indeed, it is possible to continue

**Fig. 10. End seals.** (a) Thin kidney blown out for purpose of squaring the end on a short piece of tubing. (b) Bordered ends preparatory to sealing. It is not necessary to flare ends on small tubing. (c) First blow after sealing with flared ends. (d, e) Unflared ends sealed and shrunk, before first blow. (f) One-blow finished seal resulting from initial heating like (e). (g) Second heating after stage (c) has been reached. (h) Finished seal after second blow. (i) Common error: The unsymmetrical, bulgy seal results from slightly uneven heating and rotation but is often quite usable. (j) Assembly for seal with tubes of different diameters. (k) Finished seal. The conical section is longer than need be but has been worked so that it is thick and sturdy. (l) Very common error: The seal looks good, but the narrow end of the tapered part is thin and weak.

heating after the seal has been made, blow one puff, and have a finished joint. However, such a technique requires excellent control; for most of us it is enough for the present that a square weld has been made.

Smoothing the joint usually requires two or three heatings and blows. The lump at the joint must be smoothed out. To do this, the weld is heated strongly until the lump has thickened into a slight, even constriction and is then blown out. At this point it is common to find that one side has blown out more than the other, or that a part of the periphery is actually concave. One can either assume that further rotation and heat will even out the joint, or else he can apply local heat to the bowed-in part and blow it out somewhat.

After the lumpy character of the seal has disappeared, it remains to obtain an even outer and inner diameter for the whole weld, for at this stage the glass at the seal is usually slightly blown out, and often the tubing just adjacent on either side is somewhat thinner. A large flame is employed. For the beginner this leads to trouble; the glass may sag and twist beyond control. Mastery of this technique is a milestone along the path to real facility in handling any glass. With the wide flame one can heat and blow the joint so that any gradations in thickness or size are extended over a long taper rather than the abrupt transitions resulting from use of the pointed flame. Not only does the large finishing flame lead to better-looking work, but it also gives a weld that is less liable to thermal strain.

**"Spotting" method.** Wherever possible, the rotation procedure of heating the whole joint at once should be used. In some situations this procedure is not feasible, and for these conditions the alternative "spotting" method is required. In this method the tips are heated as evenly as possible and carefully placed together, as in the previous description. Then a portion of the circumference is heated locally until any kinks at that spot shrink together and flow, and the heated area is blown out as desired. The process is repeated around the periphery. With a large glass, the whole joint must be kept hot with an auxiliary burner or by intermittent general heating, lest the joint crack before annealing. In a spotted joint, it is preferable to have a wavy outer diameter with constant wall thickness rather than a relatively even outer diameter with lumpy walls.

All glass blowing done with spot heating will have a "hammered-bronze" finish unless, after all the lumps are blown out, a larger flame is applied, and area heating and blowing is attempted. The amount that can be heated and blown at one time will vary with the size and geometric peculiarities of the work. In general it should be possible to heat a quarter of a turn, about the width of the tubing, at a time. Spotted joints will require more careful annealing than rotated welds.

**Tubes of different diameter.** To seal two tubes of different diameters, it is necessary to apply some of the fundamental operations described in preceding chapters. The smaller tube should be cut square and preferably thickened and flared somewhat at the end. The larger tube is then drawn down. With tubing up to 15 mm, it is not necessary to pull a point as a separate operation. The end can be sealed, heated at the tip over a width equal to the diameter of the smaller tube, and blown out strongly. A thin glass kidney usually results. After this kidney is lopped off with a forceps or old wire gauze, a natural flare results. If, upon first heating and blowing, it is found that the glass has not been heated enough to blow out thin, the glass is reheated, with rotation, starting at the tip and never allowing a width larger than the smaller tube to become plastic. It is always better to blow a hole on the small side rather than the large, for small holes can be flared out, but with large tubing big holes cannot be shrunk down without extensive reworking.

With large tubing, the safest procedure is to make a test-tube end, heat the tip as desired, and blow out.

For the weld, most workers find it convenient to hold the lighter, smaller tube in the hand that is brought to the mouth for blowing. In this way it is possible to see the joint while it is being blown. However, this is a matter of personal preference.

It is of prime importance to rotate each piece with the same angular velocity, so that the length of roll of the larger piece between thumb and forefinger is greater than for the smaller piece, since the angular and peripheral velocities are related by the radius. Small errors in turning can be noticed and at once corrected by observing striations in the hot twisted glass. This procedure is something that can be learned only by practice.

For the rest, the procedure is practically identical to that for two tubes of the same size. After the initial seal, it would appear to be preferable to heat slightly to the conical (large-tubing) side of the joint, always keeping the small-tube side with a slightly expanded diameter. Otherwise, and this error is very common, the place at which the small piece starts to flare is thin-walled, indented, and therefore weak.

The beginner should not be afraid to attempt heating the whole conical section with a wide flame for the final smoothing, for it is in this way that he learns to manipulate large masses of fluid glass.

**Cross-fires.** Although the technique of working with cross-fires has not been specifically discussed before, it is applicable to all the operations so far described and deserves special mention. When free rotation is possible, cross-fires give more even heating by tending to counteract the effect of jerky turns, in addition to heating the work faster. With work that is awkward to rotate, opposed flames are invaluable, for with them one can simulate the effect of rotation without actually twirling the work between thumb and forefinger. It should be understood that all manipulations except those requiring spot heating (and even some of those) can be done in cross-fires as well as with a single torch. Perhaps the one torch is better for learning, since cross-fires tend partially to cancel out the effects of uneven turning; but for competent workers they afford a saving of time and greater assurance of symmetrical work.

**T seals.** One operation in which a single flame must be used is the blowing out of a hole in a tube for a T seal. Actually, the rest of the seal can be made with cross-fires (pro-

**Fig. 11. T seals.** (a) Properly prepared cross tube. The hole is small, and the lip extends out from the tube. (b) Bad hole. (c) After seal and first blow. A few thick spots remain and must be blown out. (d) One-blow finished seal. The slight irregularities in wall thickness are not serious with small Pyrex tubing. (e) Bad seal. The joint extends on to the cross tube, and glass is folded over there, so that the seal must be worked extensively. (f) Smoothed-out seal resulting from initial weld like (b). Note that the glass has been worked mainly on the tail-tube side. (g) Result of trying to smooth out a joint like (e).

fessional glass blowers often set up large T seals on a lathe), but in most cases a single torch is preferable for the whole job.

Before starting on a T seal, everything should be in readiness. Both pieces of glass should be at hand. If the ends are to be bulged, as is usually the case when they are to be attached to rubber, the bulges should be made before the seal is started. If the ends are to be short, it is sometimes advisable to scratch them for breaking before any obstructions are present. It is wise to provide for an ample handle of glass so that the job can be manipulated without burning the hands. About 6 to 8 in. is optimum with glass up to 15 mm. Two plugs, previously tested for fit, should be on hand for the open ends.

The tail tube should have a squared end. It may be thickened and flared slightly to advantage. When this tube is in readiness, the other tube is heated at one spot. For Pyrex No. 774 up to 10 mm, no preheating is necessary; for larger glass, the usual precautions are observed. Heating for blowing out the hole is of prime importance. Almost all beginners blow out too large a hole. A very small flame is used. A novice should adjust his burner to what he thinks is the proper flame and then reduce it in size by at least half, but keeping it a hot flame. This flame is applied to the desired spot without movement until the glass shrinks markedly. Then a gentle puff—no hard blow—is given. A bulge should result. If it is smaller in diameter than the glass to be sealed on, no harm has been done. On the next heating, this bulge can be expanded by longer heating before blowing. If the bulge is too large, then the next heating should be with a very hot, small flame that melts the glass at the tip before the edges become fluid. This tip is then blown out strongly. The final hole should ideally be made away from the wall of the tube, on the protuberance of a bulge extending out from the tube. It is preferable to have a hole that is slightly too small rather than one a little too large. The tube to be sealed on will shrink down anyway when heated. True, it can be flared out for a larger hole, but such a hole usually extends part way around the tube, weakening it and also presenting a curved, not squared-off, face for sealing. With glass over 1 in., one blows a hole not over three-quarters the size of the tube to be sealed on, which is then drawn down to the same size and blown out to shape after sealing.

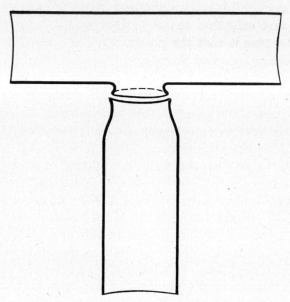

Fig. 12. Assembly for a T seal with large tubing. The hole in the cross tube is blown even smaller than shown and reamed out with a carbon to form a sturdy lip.

It is very easy in principle to complete the description of the T seal. One heats the tips, places them together, spot heats the lumps with a small flame, and smooths out the work with a larger flame. However, one or two troublesome points must be noted. The rim of the hole in the side of the tube must not be heated (before sealing) so that the lips shrink and disappear. Both this rim and the other tube end should be heated simultaneously before sealing, the former by playing back and forth in a fairly wide flame, the latter by rotation. The two glowing ends are placed together carefully, pressed slightly, and blown with slight pulling. Good one-blow seals are not uncommon, if both pieces of glass are hot enough.

Any resulting lumps are heated in a small flame. If the hole was blown properly in the first place, it will not be necessary to heat the straight tube, except at the end of the lip. If the straight tube is heated too much, it will become plastic, and the work will lose its alignment (three independent pieces of glass and only two hands to hold with!). Another fault of such heating is that the glass at the curve is blown out too far and hence becomes thinner.

When a number of T seals are to be made, especially with small tubing, it is advantageous to build a jig to hold the straight tube. With such a tool, it is possible to manipulate T seals by rotation and even to use cross-fires. The possibility of bending the straight tube is obviated. A simple jig may be made from two wall-type buret clamps or thermometer clamps.

**Y tubes.** The construction of a Y tube differs from that of a T tube only in that the "straight" tube is first bent and the hole is blown on the outside of the bend. It should be apparent that at this place the glass is thinnest, and Y seals should be attempted only on smooth, unflattened bends.

**"Suck" seals.** One technique for joining small side-arms to large glass rarely receives notice either because it is not generally known or because of the hazards encountered if the first try is not successful. This technique is the so-called *suck seal*, which can be a great aid to work in awkward spots but is not recommended for use on valuable glass apparatus without first practicing.

To make a suck seal, the side-arm is first prepared by bordering the tip and placing in the tube a wad of cotton or glass wool, loose enough to allow air passage but tight enough not to move upon sucking. The bordered end should be kept just below the softening point while the larger glass is being heated with a very hot flame about the diameter of the side-arm. When the heated spot is very hot and fluid, the small tube is placed on it so that it adheres to the hot glass and is at once sucked on strongly, so that the hot spot should expand into the side-arm and burst. If it does not break but forms a very thin bubble, the cotton may be removed and a wire inserted to puncture the bubble. If properly done, the suck seal now requires only annealing; however, it may be necessary to work the joint (in which case no advantage has been gained over the ordinary T seal). Little chips of glass from the bubble should be shaken out before the joint is worked.

If the spot has not been heated enough or if the suck is too weak, the bubble cannot be broken and the joint is spoiled. It is then necessary to heat the weld, pull off the side-arm, and start again, preferably using the ordinary procedure. For this reason the suck-seal technique is recommended only for proficient workers after much practice.

# CHAPTER VII

# The Triple, Ring, or Inner Seal; the Dewar Seal

**Supporting the glass.** To someone who has attained proficiency in making end and T seals, the ring seal should offer little that is novel in handling hot glass. Ring seals are made properly or spoiled previous to working, in the setting up. Gravity and its consequences, weight and torque, must be reckoned with, and any appreciable unsupported weight exerting a force on a flowing ring of hot glass must change that ring by thinning, twisting, bending, or otherwise moving it. A competent glass blower prevents this distortion, not by skillful manipulation, but by tying down the inner glass in a ring seal so that it will be immovable with respect to the tube in which it is enclosed while the assembly is hot. This point cannot be stressed too strongly, and it is in fact the guiding rule for all types (but one) of ring seals: Tie down the inner glass.

**Planning the work.** A second rule, equally important, is to have proper working parts. The order of work should be planned, and all parts of the assembly should be at hand. It is particularly important that any tubing ends to be incorporated in a ring seal be squared off and that small bulbs blown for the same purpose be symmetrical.

Most of the specific pieces of apparatus which require ring seals are commonly needed in the laboratory; none are beyond the skill obtainable after a few weeks of practice at the glass bench. The examples have been chosen to include as many techniques as possible, though it would be hopeless to attempt to list all the ingenious construction plans used by glass blowers.

**Flow trap. Method I.** A piece of glass which finds extensive use in the laboratory is the trap diagramed in Fig. 13. There are at least four methods of making such a trap. The first involves the glass assembly shown in Fig. 14. The important features are the symmetry of the blown-out test-tube end and its size in relation to the inner tube and bulb.

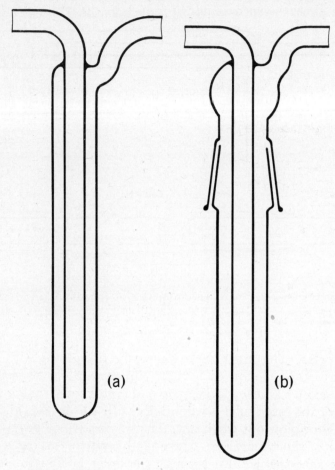

(a)          (b)

**Fig. 13. Flow trap.** (a) Usual type, construction of which is described in text. (b) Designed for frequent dismantling. A ⚤ 24/40 or 29/42 joint is suitable for outer tubing of 20- to 30-mm diameter.

The test-tube end with hole blown should make almost a right angle with the inner tube at the place to be joined. Fig. 14(a) shows the correct and Fig. 14(b) the incorrect method. If the angle is small, the outer glass at the ring seal, when heated, may shrink and stick to the inner tube away from the seal, a fatal occurrence. When the inner and outer tubes fit fairly closely, it is often advisable to blow a bulb on the end of the large tube, as shown in Fig. 14(c), so that there is room for an almost perpendicular approach at the seal.

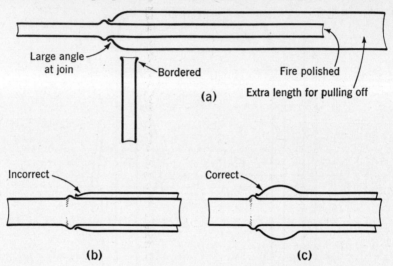

Large angle at join

Bordered

Fire polished

Extra length for pulling off

(a)

Incorrect

Correct

(b)

(c)

**Fig. 14. Flow trap. Method I.** (a) Correct assembly where clearance between tubes is at least 5 mm. Braces and blow control not shown. (b) Incorrect for small clearances. (c) Bulb blown on end—correct for small clearances. The side-arm should be sealed on the bulb.

**Braces.** The inner tube is usually tied down with 1-in. asbestos tape wound to a tight slip fit. If the asbestos is fitted tightly and the large open end is stoppered for blowing, most of the large tube is essentially without air inlet and will suck in or blow out when hot. It is necessary to provide for a hole (a short length of thin-walled capillary tubing wound in the asbestos will do) through the brace or first to seal on the side-arm, which is not in general a good procedure, especially if it is to be fairly long. A disadvantage of this method of tying the inside tube is that the asbestos does not come out easily after the job is done. Wetting the tape usually helps. Some workers prefer to use strips of asbestos paper, which can be readily shredded when wet.

A classical way of butting up the inner tube is to use a cork that just fits inside the outer tube, bored centrally for the inner tube, slotted for air passage, and with a piece of wire or string caught around it in such a way as to allow the worker to pull the cork out after the seal is finished. This procedure is also open to the objection of difficulty of cork removal, with possibility of breaking the glass.

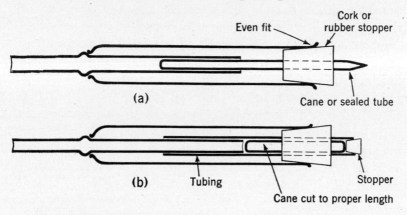

Fig. 15. **Sleeve braces.** (a) Inner sleeve, which must be held horizontally. (b) Outer sleeve with inner butt, which may be held with right end pointing down.

If the sleeve fits so tightly that air passage is impeded, a hole may be blown in an enlarged portion of the sleeve slightly past the end of the inner tube.

Another method of holding the inner tube in place, possibly the best one though not commonly used, employs a rod or tube centrally fitted in the stopper in the big tube and extending either through or over the inner tube (see Fig. 15). If an inner sleeve is used, the brace is not good if the glass is ever held vertically while hot. The best brace is an outer sleeve backed by a butt end; in this case the support works when the inner tube is pointed somewhat downward for blowing (the usual position). With all sleeve supports, the sleeve should be long enough to prevent a large wobble of the inner tube, but should also leave enough of an annular orifice so that air pressure can be transmitted to all parts.

Other types of braces will suggest themselves to the worker who becomes familiar with inner seal techniques. For instance, shredded copper can often be used (steel wool would be fine, but usually small particles dislodge themselves from the pad and stick to the hot glass).  Wooden dowels fitted with spring clips will grip the inner tubes, and so on.

The actual seal is very similar to an end seal with tubes of different diameter.  A common error is to heat too much on the large-tube side at first.  If the hole was originally made too large, a hole may be left when the first join is made.  For the first seal, the two ends are always pushed together slightly (preheating may be necessary) with a small flame applied a little bit to the small-bulb side of the seal.  The joint is always finished with a large flame.  Properly done, the seal should not have an outer ridge at the ring.

When made by rotation, ring seals require surprisingly little care in the cooling, since the inevitable strains are very evenly distributed radially.  However, they always require very slow heating for re-working, and it is best to put on the side-arm and bend it to the desired shape while the ring seal is hot and kept hot and braced, and afterwards anneal more carefully.  The side-arm is handled like any other T seal. A useful trick is to seal it on so that the top side is flush with the ring; any slight imperfections in the symmetry of the seal are far less apparent with this technique.  Any bend desired in the extension of the inner tube should also be made at this time.  Following this step, the whole area is very carefully annealed.

The trap is now finished except for the test-tube end. This part is made by methods described in Chapter V.  If the body of the trap is long enough, it is possible to rotate the glass; if not, one does the best he can.  Some glass blowers tape or clamp on a wooden handle coaxial with the trap proper. Because the test-tube end presents a problem after the side-arm has been put on, many workers prefer to close the end after the ring seal is made and then reheat the latter to put on the side-arm.

**Method II.**  Another common method of making a trap is by means of a butt seal.  The assembly, shown in Fig. 16, differs from the preceding case.  After the test-tube end has been put on the large tube, the inside tube, previously thickened and slightly flanged at the seal end, is braced with the usual precautions concerning air-pressure control for blowing. After the preliminary warming, the tip of the test tube is heated in a hot, small flame until it has shrunk and sealed to the inner tube. Heating is continued, covering only the area inside the circle made by the inner tube, until this area can be blown out. This operation can be done without changing the shape of the rest of the test-tube end at all.

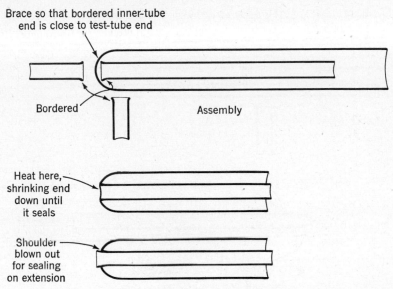

Brace so that bordered inner-tube end is close to test-tube end

Bordered    Assembly

Heat here, shrinking end down until it seals

Shoulder blown out for sealing on extension

**Fig. 16. Flow trap. Method II.** The brace is not shown.

The blown-out part, after the excess thin glass has been lopped off, should present a little shoulder for sealing on the extension. The operations involved in this seal are identical with other end-to-end seals.

**Method III.** A third method involves the assembly shown in Fig. 17. The ring seal is affected by heating the constriction, focusing a small flame just where the constriction begins to widen. The outer glass is shrunk down on the inner tube and the whole ring thickened. In this type of seal it is convenient to have separate air control for the outer annular ring, so that the outside tube glass can be blown out and does not shrink down and stick to the inner glass farther inside. If a pull is exerted at the newly made seal, the inner tube will be drawn down and also become thinner; hence, after the seal is made by shrinking, the constriction is heated on the side away from the glass to be saved until the tubes have become a solid rod, and then the glass is pulled away cautiously so that the seal is not pulled.

It is usually desirable at this stage to heat the large tube and blow it gently so that it does not "sweat down" on the

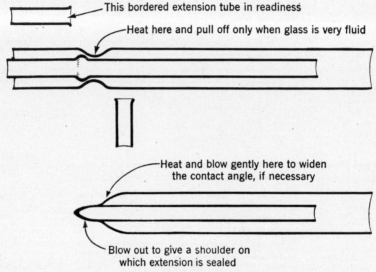

Fig. 17.   Flow trap.   Method III.

inner tube—that is, does not approach the inner tube at a small angle.

The sealed lump extending beyond the seal, when blown out, forms a natural shoulder of quite thick glass for the extension to be sealed on.   This sealing can often be accomplished without heating the actual ring seal to the softening point again.

**Method IV.**   A final method for making the ring seal in a trap is in many ways the safest.   In this procedure the inner glass is flared, instead of the outer glass being constricted. The assembly, shown in Fig. 18, involves flaring the inner tube to a close fit with the outer tube, which is previously sealed to an extension.   By judicious combination of flaring out the inner tube and shrinking the outer, any intermediate-size extension tube can be employed as desired.

The only important consideration in the original assembly, besides the ever-present bracing and blowing provision requirements, is that the flare at the end of the inner tube should end at a very sharp angle, practically perpendicular, to the tubing axis.

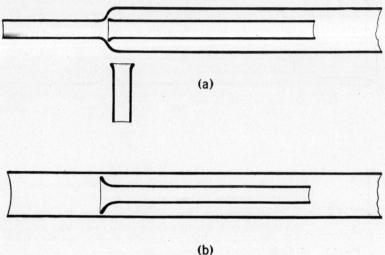

(a)

(b)

Fig. 18.  Flow trap.  Method IV.   (a) Assembly where extension is to be same diameter as inner tubing.  (b) Extension the same diameter as outer tubing.   Intermediate sizes can also be used.

The four methods described above, with slight variations, are the usual ways of making axial ring seals with appreciable weights of inner glass.   It is true that professionals sometimes make such seals without inner braces; but let the average worker try it once and he will be convinced of the necessity of bracing the inner tube in some way.

**Condensers.**  Other pieces of apparatus involving such seals are made with entirely analogous operations.   It is necessary only to plan the work in advance, providing for braces and air-pressure control at the various points.   In some cases it is advantageous to seal on small side-arms before the ring seals are made.   For instance, assemblies for making a water-jacketed condenser are shown in Fig. 19.   The butt seal is made first in each case. Pressure control in the annular ring is achieved when the second inner seal is made by use of the small side-arm already welded on the first seal. If the side-arms are sealed on first, one is stoppered with asbestos paper and the other used for blowing. Other variations will at once suggest themselves to the reader.

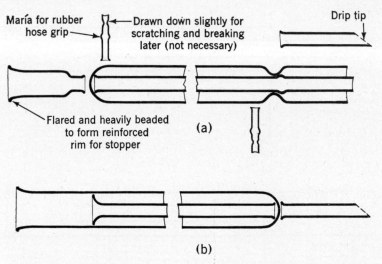

María for rubber hose grip ← Drawn down slightly for scratching and breaking later (not necessary)

Drip tip

Flared and heavily beaded to form reinforced rim for stopper

(a)

(b)

**Fig. 19. Methods of making a water-cooled condenser.** (a) Complete assembly, which should all be at hand before the ring seals are made. (b) Part of alternative assembly. The slip fits act as partial braces while the butt seals are made.

**Exercises.** Further examples of axial ring seals are legion. A few which may be mentioned, either as very common laboratory adjuncts or as glass-blowing exercises, are a glass aspirator, all-glass wash bottle with ground joint, and a double-surface condenser for very volatile solvents such as ether (see Chapter XI). The last case is particularly interesting from the planning standpoint. The seal for the water-inlet tube in the cold finger requires some thought. At least three methods of bracing are possible, one involving the use of copper gauze, which can later be dissolved in nitric acid.

When the inner tube is very light or short, it is not necessary to brace it in any way. The cut-off seal at the bottom of a McLeod gauge (which is necessary for precise low-pressure use of the gauge) is simply made by slipping the inner ring, fitted closely to the outer tube, into place and heating at the contact point, blowing the outer tube back to shape (see Fig. 50).

**Other traps.**  A Kjeldahl trap (Fig. 20) can be made from the accompanying assembly.  The inner tube will wobble somewhat during blowing but, because of its small weight,

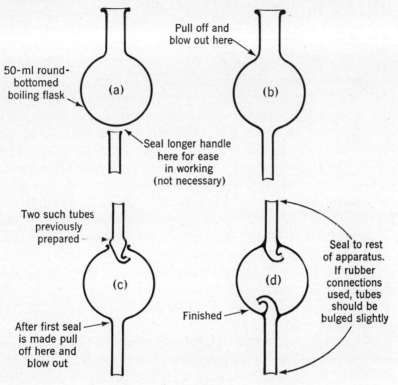

Fig. 20.  Steps in the construction of a Kjeldahl trap.

will not be distorted badly at the seal unless the joint is worked a great deal.

When dealing with mercury, it is often useful to put an overflow and return trap into the line.  This trap is similar to a Kjeldahl trap, with the addition of a hole in the inner tube just inside the seal for overflow return.

The ring seals in the glass torches shown in Fig. 2 do not require braces during construction.

**Ring seals through the side of a tube.** Ring seals through the side of a tube are formally similar to T seals. The seal is made by the butt technique, with the inner tube very firmly braced. A shoulder should be blown out for the extension-tube seal; that is, the extension tube should not be welded directly onto the seal. Such seals are really quite easy to make if the inner tube is immovable. However, they are the most strained of all glass joints, and it is necessary to keep the whole area, including a wide ring of the outer tube, hot while the glass is being worked and to cool the heated area very slowly and evenly.

**Gas flowmeter.** As an example of the use of this type of seal, a gas flowmeter is shown in Fig. 21. This flowmeter has several advantages: It is easy to mount, sturdy, and compact, and it has several different ranges because of the replaceable capillaries. If the inner tube is small with respect to the outer, only the inner-tube liquid height need be read except in very precise work.

**Dewar seal.** One other type of seal that, though not formally similar, involves the same basic techniques as the triple seal is the Dewar seal. In this type of seal, two glass tubes, usually coaxial, one inside the other, are sealed together at one end, but without an extension jutting through as in a ring seal. In many cases it is feasible to make a ring seal, cutting the extension off close to the seal, rather than the Dewar-type weld.

In setting up a Dewar seal, it is necessary to brace the glass tightly, providing for air-pressure control, and to have the glass rims to be sealed in close and even juxtaposition. The inner and outer lips should be cut square. Following this step, one procedure is to flange out the inner tube to a right angle, so that the lip hits the outer tube edge, as in Fig. 22(a). The outer lip can even be flanged back on itself, as in Fig. 22(d).

It may be necessary, for the initial join, to use a little welding rod. No new types of operations are involved in the blowing or annealing. Practically the only stumbling block with properly set up and braced work is overheating at the seal so that the glass shrinks and sticks together below the joint. It is often desirable to blow a little annular bulge at the seal to prevent such an occurrence.

The alternative method involves shrinking in the outer piece rim rather than flanging the inner, as in Fig. 22(c),

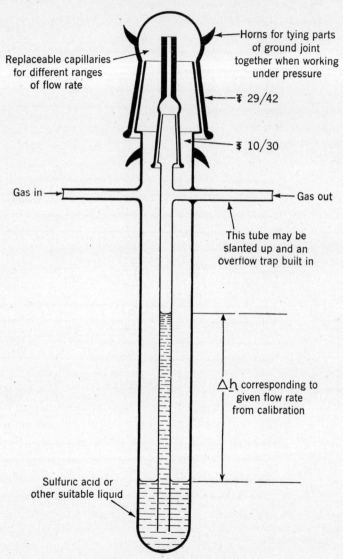

Horns for tying parts of ground joint together when working under pressure

Replaceable capillaries for different ranges of flow rate

$ 29/42

$ 10/30

Gas in →

Gas out

This tube may be slanted up and an overflow trap built in

$\triangle h$ corresponding to given flow rate from calibration

Sulfuric acid or other suitable liquid

Fig. 21.   Gas flowmeter.

but is definitely not recommended, since the shrunken outer rim will be very thick, and also the seal will be made where it is hard to play the flame.  A combination of the two methods, resulting in the assembly of Fig. 22(b), is easy to work in the flame.

Dewar seals are used in making the familiar Dewar flasks, in one design of the boiler of diffusion pumps, and in tempera-

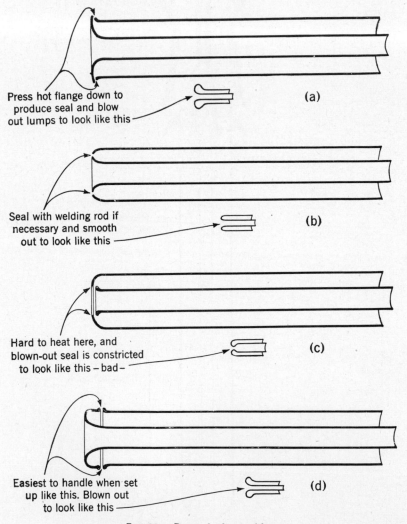

Press hot flange down to produce seal and blow out lumps to look like this ⟶  (a)

Seal with welding rod if necessary and smooth out to look like this ⟶  (b)

Hard to heat here, and blown-out seal is constricted to look like this – bad –  (c)

Easiest to handle when set up like this. Blown out to look like this ⟶  (d)

Fig. 22.   Dewar-seal assemblies.

ture-probe wells on all types of apparatus. In this case a ring seal can often be substituted. Fig. 23 shows boiling flasks with a Dewar-seal and ring-seal well. The ring seal is first

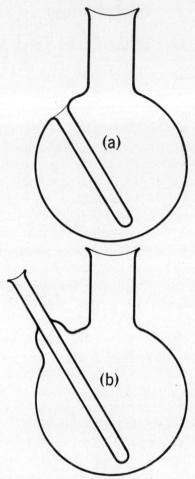

Fig. 23. Thermometer wells in boiling flasks. (a) Dewar-seal type. (b) Ring-seal type.

made with a convenient outer tube, as in a trap. The outer tube is then cut off fairly close to the seal and then welded to the flask as a T seal, care being taken not to heat the inner tube enough to deform it. Thorough annealing is required. The Dewar seal is a good exercise to test ingenuity in planning.

# CHAPTER VIII
## Use of the Hand Torch

**Situations requiring hand torch.** Many situations occur in which it is desirable to keep glass in place and use a movable flame; on the vacuum bench it is necessary. Though the principles involved are the same as for stationary flame-movable glass operations, a few points should be specifically noted. The first rule is always to have welding rod at hand. Two- or 3-mm cane, drawn down from larger rod if necessary, is not an accessory to be ashamed of; indeed, in finishing closed circuits, professionals use it liberally.

Only the simplest operations should be attempted in place. End seals with both tubes of approximately the same diameter and **T** seals are, with practically no exceptions, the whole repertory of in-place glass blowing.

From the esthetic standpoint, since hot glass sags, end seals should be made with the tubes vertical and **T**'s upright. This procedure should especially be followed with larger glass, which must be worked a good deal to remove lumps. However, hand-torch work is seldom neat anyway with large tubing. Presumably such work is always clamped tightly in place and is not subject to mechanical shock, so that thin spots are not too troublesome.

**Both glass ends clamped.** Two cases must be considered: That in which both pieces of glass are clamped in place, and that in which one piece is free. In the first case it is of prime importance that the ends be squared off and clamped in juxtaposition, with a slight pressure tending to push them together. As gentle heating is applied all around, the glass should shove together. Once sealed, such a joint is easy to finish—first the pinpoint flame to fuse the kinks, then a larger flame for finishing, and finally even application of heat to the whole joint to bring it to the softening temperature, so that strains due to clamps are relieved. The possibility that holes will be left in the original seal is always present; in such a case it is necessary to use welding rod, but as sparingly as possible to prevent lumpiness. It is always better to blow bulges than to leave lumps of glass in a seal.

**One end free.** If a short, light, or easy-to-handle end of glass is to be sealed on at the side or bottom of another piece of stationary glass, it is often convenient to hold the end in one hand, rather than clamping it, while manipulating the torch with the other. In this way the original seal can usually be effected without the use of welding rod, by bending or shoving at the plastic juncture. The rubber-tubing blow-piece should either be attached to the stationary glass or hang from the other end without exerting appreciable torque for the hand to overcome. This method is more rapid than the preceding one, but it requires more practice and skill. The technique should not be attempted with short leads to be sealed on top of stationary glass. Hot-air burns can be quite serious.

When a seal made in the above manner is subsequently clamped, it is desirable to heat a ring of glass (not necessarily at the seal) to the softening point. Strains due to clamping are a common cause of glass failure. It should be a general rule to clamp glass rigidly in as few places as is consistent with applied weight and bending force. Glass should never be clamped directly to metal, except with the special clamps for spherical joints.

**Closing a circuit.** Closing a circuit of tubing is an interesting application of the hand torch. The method usually recommended is to insert a prefabricated piece in place, one end being joined temporarily with a short rubber sleeve. The other end is sealed, the rubber cut off with a razor blade, and the final seal made. Here welding glass is always needed. The lazy man's variant of this technique is to join one end without blowing, make the other seal, and then return to the first, reheating very slowly, since the unblown weld is almost certainly strained.

Closed circuits are particularly susceptible to cooling

strains.    After all the seals are made, a length of the smallest glass in the circuit should be kept at the softening point for some time.    If permissible in the equipment design, it is desirable to include an expansion coil or bellows in the closed circuit.

**Sealing *in vacuo*.**    One hand-torch technique that deserves special mention is sealing off *in vacuo*.    This technique is not difficult if the constriction is properly made.    It should be long and tapered, if possible, with fairly thick walls.    A soft flame is moved around the constriction, with continuous pull on the apparatus to be sealed off.    Even peripheral heating will give a seal that is not sucked in on one side. It is possible to seal off tubing up to 10-mm o.d. without a constriction in this way.

If the evacuated vessel is tightly supported and cannot be pulled away, the job is more difficult.    It is desirable to have a constriction as long and as narrow of bore as possible. A long, thin section can then be heated until it sucks and shrinks into a rod.    The middle of this section is then strongly heated and pulled away with a tweezers or another piece of glass, severing the connection.

Annealing seal-offs is a rather touchy procedure, since the relatively thin glass away from the seal cannot be heated to the give point, lest it suck in.    However, annealing is apparently not too critical with Pyrex No. 774.

**Special torches.**    On some glass blowers' benches one sees a special torch for in-place seals on tubing up to ½-in. o.d.   It is really a movable miniature version of cross-fires, and by playing it about the seal one is able to heat the whole periphery quite evenly.    Such a double-flame torch, sometimes called a *splicing torch*, is not common, but it does have its uses where much in-place work is done.    Most workers have never seen a splicing torch but would probably agree that it is a superior tool to the usual single flame for smoothing out seals and vacuum seal-offs.    Anyone with a little ingenuity, time, and skill can design and build one from metal or glass.    The splicing torch in Fig. 1 is made from the base (including mixing chamber) of a commercial torch and two inexpensive commercial tips brazed on to bent copper tubes.

**High-vacuum leaks.** The important problem of sealing tiny leaks in systems requiring high vacuum is properly treated under hand-torch manipulation, since most vacuum equipment is clamped in place. Before describing the techniques, however, a digression into the causes of such leaks and the methods of finding them will be of value.

Leaks which will hold liquid but not vacuum are commonly caused by occlusion of asbestos, iron oxide, or other foreign matter in a joint and sometimes by a hole in the original seal that has not been worked enough, especially where much welding rod has been employed. Their occurrence is noted by pumping out the system and measuring the ultimate vacuum or by shutting out the pump and watching for a rise in pressure. Neither of these methods tells the exact leak spot, which can be found with a spark coil (also known as a Tesla coil, brush discharge, leak tester, vacuum tester, or detector). The discharge from the tip of the instrument, when placed against a glass container, will start a weak reddish glow discharge on the inside of the glass when the pressure is diminished to about 1 mm Hg. This glow becomes stronger as the pressure is lowered further and disappears at about $5 \times 10^{-4}$ mm. If mercury is present, the discharge is purple at higher pressures and blue below $10^{-1}$ mm.

If there is a capillary leak in the glass, the spark coil will induce a very bright, practically white, discharge through it. A very strong spark will actually punch a hole through a thin spot, but this is just as well, since such thin glass is liable to be troublesome.

To repair such a leak, the system is let down to atmospheric pressure, blow control provided, and the bad spot heated with the hand torch. If the leak was caused by insufficient working of the joint, it can usually be cured by heating and blowing a few times. If, however, foreign matter is embedded in the glass, it is necessary to cover over the leak path with a dot of welding rod. In any case the glass should be thickened by heating strongly, and then it should be thoroughly annealed.

Leaks which occur in glass that is not to be heated or cooled and in which chemical cleanliness is not important can be sealed up with picein, sealing wax, or de Khotinsky cement. The application is made by warming the glass (not the wax), applying the stick of sealing compound, and gently heating the applied daub to smooth it over.

# CHAPTER IX

## Other Operations

A NUMBER of miscellaneous glass operations that have not been covered in the previous chapters crop up from time to time in the laboratory. A brief discussion of most of these operations appears valuable, since they are, in the main, simple enough to be mastered by the average technician. A few more manipulations, which are more advanced but which nonetheless must sometimes be used in devising certain types of equipment, are also included.

**Constrictions.** Constrictions in tubing, such as in manometer tubes, are very commonly encountered. The obvious variable ratios are (1) original bore to constricted bore and (2) original wall thickness to constriction wall thickness. It is possible to vary these ratios within wide limits. Ratio (1) is determined by the flow rate desired; ratio (2) is the strength factor and should be large for small tubing and at least unity for large tubing (constricted bore over 10 mm). Diagrams of different types of constrictions are given in Fig. 24.

Types *a* and *b* are made by heating a tube with rotation and slight compressional pressure of both hands. No blowing is necessary if the heating is done carefully. If *a* is desired, but the glass is pushed so much that *b* results, the tube can be removed from the flame and pulled slightly. It may then be necessary to reheat it in a large flame and blow to thicken the glass at the edge of the constriction, which will become thin when pulled. A constriction that has been shrunk too far can be blown gently to the desired orifice unless it has actually shrunk into a rod.

It is not feasible, with large glass, to make a constriction of type *a* or *b*, since the large lump of solid glass is apt to be strained. Large glass is handled as in pulling a point, making sure that the glass has shrunk and thickened before pulling, so that the walls will not be too thin after pulling.   For very small constrictions in large tubing, a short length of thick-walled capillary should be sealed between two pieces of the large tubing, as in *d*.

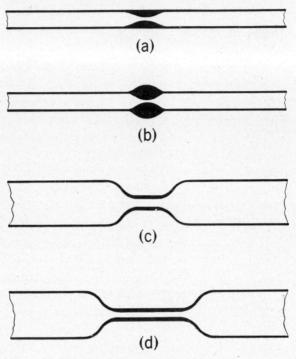

Fig. 24.   Constrictions in tubing.

**Capillary.**   Thick-walled capillary requires care in initial heating and in preparation before joints are made.   The inner bore at an end to be sealed should always be enlarged, and also the wall thickness should be lessened.   Though this can be done with a waxed-wire flaring tool, the easiest way is to seal off, blow a small bulb on the end, and then blow out the bulb.   These operations are diagramed in Fig. 25.   Consequently, in sealing these tubes, it is never necessary to heat to softening any glass with an inner bore smaller than that of the main tubing.   The inner bore at the seal is shrunk to the desired size after the joint has been sealed and smoothed, as the last operation.

**Capillary T seals.**   Capillary T seals are rather difficult. If it is permissible to introduce the extra volume, a small, thick-walled bulb should be blown in the straight tube at

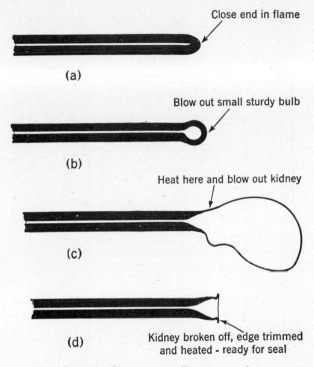

Fig. 25.   Preparing capillary for a seal.

the point at which the seal is to be made, and the pre-flanged and tapered tail tube should be sealed at a hole blown in the bulb.   Under any circumstances it is desirable to flare and taper the wall of the tail tube.   It can be shrunk to original size after the seal is finished.

Regular tubing joints to capillary are analogous to different-diameter joints.   Again it is necessary only to flare the capillary at the end so that glass with a small inner bore is never softened during the seal.

**Sharp bends.**   Sharp bends in one piece of large tubing are invariably unsuccessful; two reliable methods for accomplishing the same end will be indicated, as shown in Fig. 7. In the first, a test-tube end is blown at the point at which the bend is desired, and the rounded end is flattened either by sucking gently while the end is hot or pressing it with a carbon paddle.   Then a hole is blown out on the side wall,

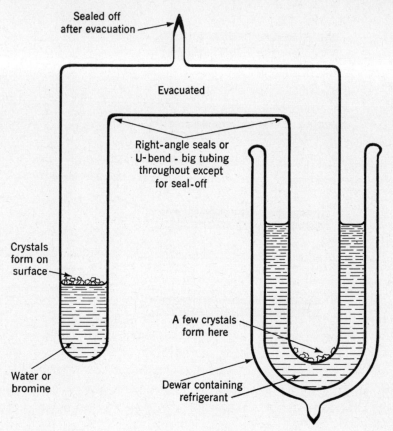

Fig. 26.  Cryophorus.

just at the end, and another piece is sealed on as in a **T** seal. In the second method, two ends to be sealed are ground to a 45° angle and welded by the spotting technique and finally heated with a large flame for smoothing.   As an example of the use of large-tubing bends, a cryophorus is shown in Fig. 26.  Water or bromine is introduced, frozen, evacuated (the cryophorus is usually subsequently warmed, again frozen, and pumped to outgas it), and sealed *in vacuo*. It serves as a nice demonstration of the heat of vaporization, since a refrigerant placed about the empty arm almost at once causes the liquid in the other arm to freeze at its surface.

**Coils.** Glass coils may be made in the laboratory in two ways. With either method success is not assured, since the proper heating and turning "feel" is rather touchy. A very large, even flame (or vertical cross-fires) is desirable, and even then it takes specialized techniques to coil tubing over 10-mm o.d.

**Free-hand.** In the first method, the glass is worked free-hand. A sharp right-angle bend is made far enough from the end—say, 6 or 8 in.—to leave a handle of tubing. Then the tubing is fed with one hand through the wide flame while the other rotates the handle. If the flame, feed rate, and rotation are nicely balanced, an even coil will result. Often the first two or three turns are not quite circular; they may be cut off and a new end sealed on.

**Mandrel.** In the other method, a mandrel is used. A mandrel is a glass or metal cylinder of slightly under the desired diameter (sometimes slightly tapered to facilitate removal of the coil), wrapped evenly with wet asbestos paper, smoothed down at the seams, and allowed to dry thoroughly. Nickel or carbon mandrels need not be asbestos-covered. A little water-glass (sodium silicate) solution may be painted on the asbestos. A metal mandrel can be notched at the end to start the coil; the end of the tube to be coiled is fused to the tip of a glass mandrel. If available, rollers should be used to steady the weight of the mandrel while the glass is being heated, as in the preceding method, and rolled on the large cylinder. In general, a new asbestos covering must be used for each coil. A coil is designed and the mandrel put together on one day, and the mandrel is used the next day after drying.

Glass coils find uses in condensers, to take up strain in closed circuits, to provide flexibility in all-glass shaking devices, and to bring water through long paths for high-voltage cooling requirements.

**Expansion bellows.** Expansion bellows are also used to take up strains in glass. When an inner and an outer jacket are sealed together, either by Dewar or ring seals, and

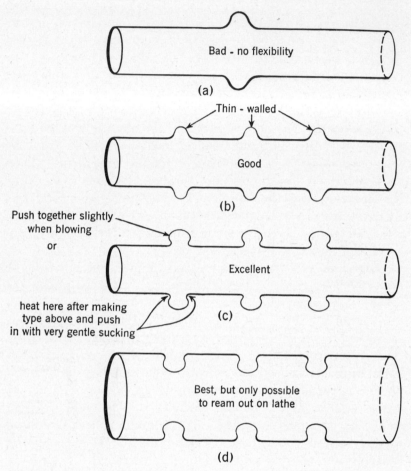

**Fig. 27. Types of expansion bellows.** Type (b) is the one commonly used in the laboratory. (c) and (d) are ordinarily done on lathes; the latter is coming into vogue on commercially designed fractionating-column vacuum jackets.

one is to be run at a temperature varying greatly from the other, or even with any double ring seals on very wide tubing, it is desirable to compensate for expansion due to differential heating by blowing bellows in the outer glass. Bellows are merely fairly thin bulbs and are commonly seen on vacuum jackets for fractional distillation columns and condenser jackets of wide-nozzle diffusion pumps. A very sophisticated use of such a bellows is to provide for the controlled mechanical motion of the valve needle in an all-glass greaseless vacuum valve.

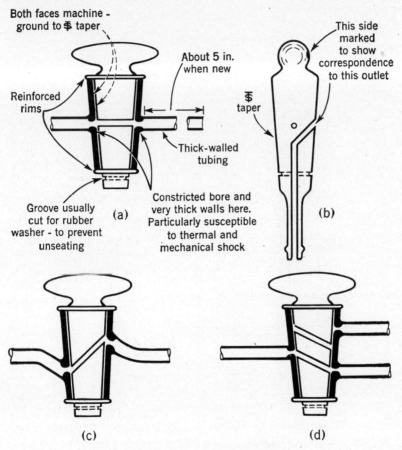

Fig. 28. Standard types of stopcocks.

**Ground joints.** The ever-increasing use of ground-glass joints—stopcocks, conical joints, and spherical joints—makes it desirable to include a section on them. In addition to the standard types of stopcocks shown in Fig. 28, many special stopcocks are now made. A few of these are shown in Fig. 29. Particular attention may be called to the illustrated high-pressure stopcock, which solves the problem of flow in the range of 1 to 5 atmospheres or more, and the vacuum-type manifold stopcocks, whose impedance to pumping is less than other types. Almost all stopcocks are now made with replaceable barrels and plugs, usually symbolized by a $\overline{\$}$ (standard taper) or similar marking.[1]

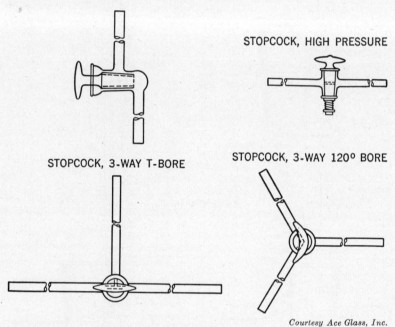

STOPCOCK, HIGH VACUUM, MERCURY SEAL

STOPCOCK, HIGH PRESSURE

STOPCOCK, 3-WAY T-BORE

STOPCOCK, 3-WAY 120° BORE

*Courtesy Ace Glass, Inc.*

**Fig. 29.   Some special stopcocks.**

In Fig. 30 are shown two unusual conical joints, not illustrated elsewhere. These are also precision ground to a 1:10 taper for interchangeability.[1] The first number stamped on a conical joint (as in $\overline{\$}$ 24/40) indicates the width of the circular ring at the top of the joint in millimeters, and the second the length of the ground surface. Joints with the ground surfaces "metalized" with a thin film of platinum or gold bonded to the glass can also be obtained commercially.

---

[1] Specifications are given in the National Bureau of Standards Bulletin CS 21–39.

Interchangeable joints accurately ground to a hemi-spheroidal surface are an outstanding new development, since they can be used at angles other than head-on approach.

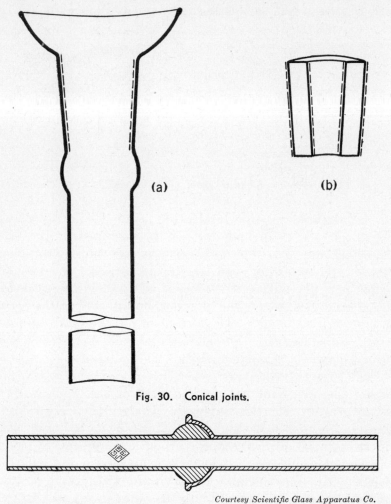

(a)　　　　　　　　　　　　(b)

Fig. 30.　Conical joints.

Fig. 31.　Sectional view showing construction of spherical ball-and-socket joint.

They should find extensive use in complicated assemblies that must be dismantled from time to time. They are designated by two numbers (as 28/15), the first indicating the diameter of the spherical form on which they are ground, in millimeters, and the second indicating the bore of the extension.    A new type of patented clamp for spherical joints[2] is superior to the original clamps made for them.

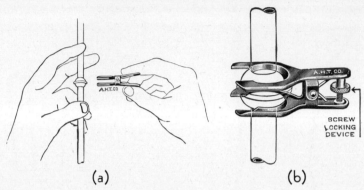

(a)                                    (b)

Fig. 32.  Clamps for spherical joints.   (a) For  sizes  12 and 18.   (b) For larger sizes.

## Lubrication.

**Lubrication.**  Before lubrication, ground surfaces should be absolutely clean and dry.  With a stopcock, the plug is gently warmed (but not near a smoky flame) to about 35° C, and two thin, even longitudinal streaks of grease are applied, a few millimeters wide, running down between the holes on either side.   The plug is then inserted in the warm barrel with the plug in the valve open position and compressional force applied.   The lubricant should then flow evenly over the whole ground surface.   The plug should not be turned to spread the grease, since this procedure may trap air, unless the lubricant has not spread over the whole surface after pressure has been applied.   Under this circumstance the plug is turned back and forth from 5° to 10° only, with pressure, until air has escaped without entrapment.

Conical and spherical joints are lubricated in analogous fashion, the inner member being ringed with grease near its tubulation end and pressed into the outer to squeeze out air.

In vacuum systems (except when vacuums better than $10^{-5}$ mm Hg are required) and in other places in which added rigidity is required and joints are seldom removed, sealing wax (red banker's specie type) makes a fine, vacuum-tight, and sturdy joint.   The glass, rather than the wax, should

[2] Distributed by Arthur H. Thomas Co., Philadelphia.

be heated before application. Cold sealing wax has no action on a mercury surface. In the frontispiece, two spherical joints and the conical joint cap on the tipping McLeod gauge have been sealed with banker's specie wax.

**Manipulation of ground joints.** When glass is being worked near any ground surface, it must always be grease-free. Asbestos plugs should be used for stoppers, and two hot ground surfaces should not come into contact. For instance, if one part of a conical joint is used as a handle for the other while the first is being worked, the surfaces should be separated by asbestos paper or tape. Stopcock barrels should be withdrawn and asbestos plugs inserted. Handles for ball-and-socket joints should be glass tubes inserted inside the joint with a tight-fitting sleeve of asbestos.

A good general rule is that glass may not be worked closer than one diameter's length from a ground surface without distorting it. Even then it is necessary to be careful to avoid warping the ground part. In many cases, for the sake of strength and freedom from strains, it is advisable to heat the work as usual and afterwards regrind the surface as explained below. One exception to this procedure is in sealing very close to stopcocks in certain situations. They are particularly susceptible to thermal cracks where the tubulations are sealed to the barrel, and it is often advisable to wrap the outside thoroughly with wet asbestos paper and work the joint with a tiny flame. In this way, if the paper is thoroughly moistened, the stopcock itself never gets above 100° C. Although such joints have some strain, they practically never crack. The above statement applies only to Pyrex, of course.

**Grinding; refinishing.** For refinishing previously ground surfaces that are suspected of having been warped by heating, fine carborundum powder or its equivalent is used. Any mesh from 400 to 600 is suitable. Both surfaces are wetted with a liquid vehicle, one is dipped lightly in the powder, and then the two surfaces are ground together, three or four revolutions being completed in one direction before rotation is reversed. Only a small amount of grinding is necessary; the most common error is overgrinding. Turpentine or a

5 per cent solution of camphor in turpentine is the usually recommended vehicle.   Water does nicely for all but polished surfaces, for which pumice and rouge are needed, along with specialized techniques that are not treated here.

**Rough grinding.**   For rough grinding, the most desirable setup is a power-driven horizontal grindstone fed with carborundum and water.   A suitable mesh is 120; 60 mesh tends to chip glass.   Lacking this, as most laboratories do, a heavy glass or metal plate charged with carborundum will do.   Here the glass rather than the plate is moved.   For finishing the work, a fresh section of plate charged with finer mesh is used.

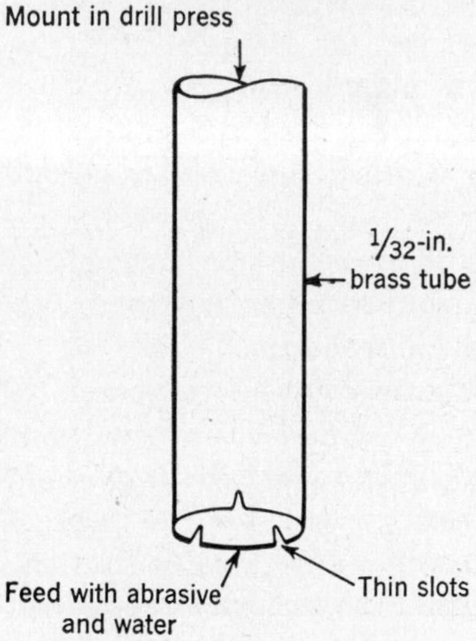

Mount in drill press

$\frac{1}{32}$-in. brass tube

Feed with abrasive and water

Thin slots

**Fig. 33.   Drilling large holes in glass.** Light pressure is alternately applied and removed.  A slow-speed drill press is used.

**Drilling.**   If an apparatus is such that a proper hole cannot be blown in it, it can be drilled by twirling a copper wire charged with carborundum or by careful handling in a drill press, with very little pressure and plenty of abrasive.

**Marking glass.**   Glass can be marked in various ways. Diamond-tipped pencils are available, although they are not seen in many laboratories.   They leave a rather thin, frosty mark.   The usual procedure of coating glass with paraffin, writing through with a needle, and then etching with hydrofluoric acid leaves a clear, not easily visible indentation if aqueous HF is used.   Hydrogen fluoride gas gives a frosted mark but is even more touchy to handle than the water solution.   A very easy and satisfactory method for making simple marks like graduated lines is to rub with a string or copper wire on the wet, abrasive-coated glass.   Vibratory glass-marking pencils with a diamond or hard-steel point have recently come on the market.

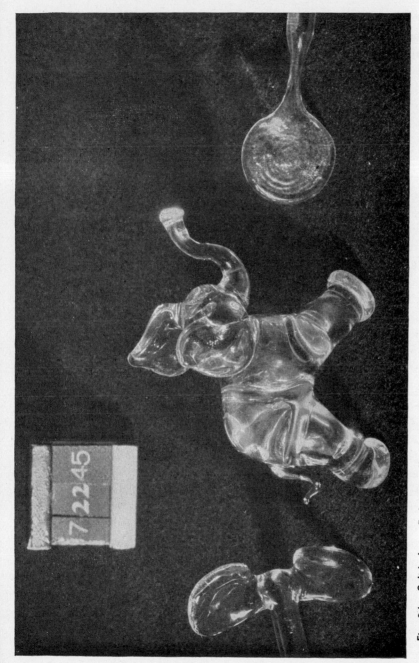

**Fig. 34. Solid glass.** Left, propeller-type stirrer with upward pitch for clockwise drive. Right, pressed disc of glass from which stirrer blade is formed. Center, solid glass work as a hobby. The date marker in the background is included for size comparison; it is exactly one inch long.

**Solid glass.**  Solid glass cannot be blown, of course, but is worked by pushing and pulling, or squeezing between carbon paddles or forceps.  Big lumps of solid glass will require careful annealing.  In addition to being made into utilitarian objects such as stirrers, solid glass can be fashioned into "sculptured" forms like statues, and thus offers itself as a medium for an interesting hobby.

**Stirrers.**  To make a stirrer, the end of a glass rod is rotated in the flame until a spherical lump forms.  It is at once pressed between carbon plates until it has flattened into a disc.  The junction of the disc and rod handle is heated, and the former is grasped with a forceps and pulled until only a thin connection remains.  Two such discs, still connected to their handles, are made.  These discs are attached to a small globe of glass on the tip of the stirrer shaft, both parts of each weld being heated before joining.  The handles are pulled off and the blades fashioned by squeezing, pushing, and pulling off hot glass.  Any shape and pitch can be made.  Lumpy joins are smoothed by intense local heat, since really hot glass flows like honey to form a smooth surface.  Very large stirrer blades can be made if a glass saw is available.  A ring of 40-mm tubing, about 20 mm wide, is cut off and then cut to form two half circles, one of which is turned about and sealed to the other to form a large curved blade.

**Vitreous silica.**  Silica glass[3] is used in cases in which very high temperatures are encountered or special chemical inertness is required, and in photochemical applications in which transmission of ultraviolet light is desired.  Silica glass in transparent form can be purchased for photochemical work or in a translucent or satin-like opaque form for the first two general uses given above.

Silica softens only at very high temperatures and has a very small working range.  In consequence it is necessary to use an oxy-hydrogen flame for tubing of 7-mm o.d. and larger,

---

[3] Referring to fused or vitreous silica as "quartz" is a common error.  Silica is the name given to the chemical, silicon dioxide ($SiO_2$), which in any form can be made into a glass, whereas quartz is a *crystalline* form of silica, the properties of which are distinctly different from the vitreous form.  Silica glass cannot be sealed directly to quartz, which shatters on sudden heating.

and usually to blow while the heated spot is in the flame. Offsetting these disadvantages are the facts that silica has an extremely low expansion coefficient and hence requires no annealing, and that it is harder and mechanically stronger than any other glass.

The blinding white light of hot silica makes it necessary to use dark goggles when working it, and the intense heat may require a special mask for shielding the face.

**Vycor.** Recently a new glass, "Vycor" (Corning Nos. 790 and 792), has appeared on the market. Made from an ordinary type of glass by a special process that leaches out the majority of metals present, Vycor contains approximately 96 per cent silica and has properties approaching those of the pure fused chemical. It can be advantageously employed in many cases as a substitute for the more expensive silica, which is difficult to manufacture.

**Seals.** Silica seals are almost invariably made by the spot-heating technique, unless lathe facilities are at hand. Using the hand torch, one clamps the larger piece in place, welds on one spot of the smaller piece, and finishes the seal with use of silica welding rod as necessary. After a small portion of the periphery has fused together and cooled slightly, it is not necessary to brace the smaller piece, since the welded spot will not become hot enough to flow again without direct, intense heat.

The seal can be smoothed somewhat by blowing. Silica should be blown while it is in the flame, with very gentle puffs, owing to its high, short working range. If blown too hard, it will blow out. However, if this occurs, it is only necessary to patch the hole with welding rod, a repair that is much easier with silica than with Pyrex.

**Bends.** It is impossible to bend silica by the techniques used for soft glass or Pyrex. A small section of the periphery is heated and bent slightly, another section heated and bent, and so on. Kinks and flat spots are then smoothed as well as possible by spot heating. It is obvious that the concave side will be thick and lumpy and the convex side thin and flattened. However, owing to the low coefficient of expansion and the great mechanical strength of silica, neither of these defects, which would be serious with soft glass or even Pyrex, detracts from the usefulness of a silica bend.

**Graded seals.**   For fusing silica to Pyrex No. 774, a graded seal is necessary.   While serviceable graded seals can be made at the glass bench, it is preferable to use the tested commercial article.   Even though they are expensive, so few are needed and they are so superior to the homemade kind that it is certainly advisable to employ them.

In the laboratory, graded seals are made by sealing in order, starting at the silica end, silica, Corning glasses 790, 723, 720, 724, and 774.   The 720–724 seal is hardest to work because 720 softens 300° higher than 724, but it may not be as strained as the 724–774 seal, in which the difference in expansion coefficients is greatest.   In an emergency, graded seals can be made by fusing together batches of ground-up silica and 774 in the proportions 4:1, 3:1, 2:1, 1:1, 1:2, 1:3, and 1:4, stirring the melts for thorough mixing, drawing them out into welding rod, and applying successive rings of the mixtures in order on a silica tube of the desired diameter. One can also add enough of each batch to close off the end, blow it out into a kidney, trim the edge, and apply the next glass.   This method allows the different mixtures to flow together better than in the technique of adding rings.

Simple breaks in graded seals can be repaired by careful manipulation, especially if the broken ends fit together well. The Pyrex No. 774 portion should be held below the silica end, since heat conduction in air is upwards.   Otherwise the 774 part will soften and flow before the silica end is hot enough to work.

**Devitrification.**   Owing to the crystallization of silica on rapid cooling, a cloudy area is often observed after heating, especially at the edges of the worked portion.   This cloudiness is almost always a surface phenomenon and does no harm except in cases in which light transmission is important. Rinsing the area with a hydrofluoric acid solution will usually clear up the milkiness.

# CHAPTER X
## Glass-to-Metal Seals

THE direct joining of glass to various metals involves manipulations that are no more difficult than those required in
making a T seal or perhaps a simple ring seal; yet the principles
which must be followed are in general so poorly recognized
by laboratory technicians that such seals are a common
stumbling block to many otherwise proficient glass blowers.

**General principles; glass must wet metal.** To make a successful glass-to-metal seal, it is necessary to insure that the
glass will bond to the metal—that is, that the hot, plastic
glass will wet, flow into, and form an adhesive union with the
metal surface. This requirement always makes it necessary
to de-gas the metal, since all metals adsorb large amounts of
gases on their surfaces. The adsorbed gases, if not previously
"boiled," off, will vaporize while the seal is being worked and
give rise to bubbles at the interface, which will be imperfectly
bonded, strained, and may have capillary leak paths.

**The oxide film.** Although some controversy still arises
over the point, it is generally conceded that glasses do not
bond to metals at a surface but rather to their oxides, the
possible exception being platinum. It is therefore necessary
to oxidize a metal surface before sealing to glass (with platinum, which forms a surface oxide only under specialized
conditions, this is questionable). On the other hand, since
metals are not usually isomorphous with their oxides, a thick
oxide coat may lead to a porous, brittle, and mechanically
weak seal. The proper degree of oxidation is a critical factor
in making glass-to-metal seals with desired properties.

**Thermal expansion.** As pointed out in Chapter I, the
expansion coefficients of glasses rise markedly as they are
heated. Even if a glass and a metallic element have the same
thermal expansion coefficient at relatively low temperatures,
their seal will still be somewhat strained because their expan-

sion characteristics will be different at working temperatures. Only with the Kovar and Fernico alloys, the expansion characteristics of which were successfully engineered to resemble those of glasses, is an unstrained glass-to-metal seal possible. Two types of seals with metallic elements will nonetheless work. The first is one in which the expansion coefficients of the given glass and metal are close enough so that the seal, though strained, is mechanically strong enough to resist the breaking forces set up upon cooling. The second type, in which materials with quite different expansion coefficients are sealed, depends upon the use of a very thin piece of metal, preferably with a low yield point, so that the large cooling strains are relieved by the deformation of the metal rather than the cracking of the glass. This type of seal is possible practically only with metals that are ductile and malleable at room temperature.

With the foregoing in mind, the actual manipulations in making glass-to-metal seals described in the following discussion should be considered in terms of the principles underlying them as well as the empirical experience that has shown them to be workable procedures.

**Platinum.** The coefficients of expansion of platinum and some soft glasses at low temperatures are practically identical, and vacuum-tight seals between them may be made with little strain. Lead glass appears to wet the metal better than lime glass and should be used if possible.

The wire is first heated orange-red at the spot at which the seal is to be made to de-gas the surface as much as possible. It should be remembered that metals are good heat conductors, so that the platinum should be handled with a pin vise, forceps, or a handle of thin cane to which the platinum has been sealed at a low temperature so that the rod can later be cracked away cleanly. Platinum melts at a relatively low temperature and should never directly receive the full heat of the torch more than momentarily. Platinum does not oxidize appreciably, and no unusual precautions need be taken to insure a clean metal surface other than the first heating.

A bead of lead glass is then fused to the wire. The preferred method is to slip a small tube over the wire. This sleeve is then heated strongly to obtain a good metal-glass bond. The sleeve should be heated from one end to the other so as not to entrain any gas bubbles. A bead may also be made by wrapping a thin cane around the wire. For ease in making electrical contact later, the end of the wire may be looped, and the bead applied at the tip of the eyelet, as shown in Fig. 35(b).

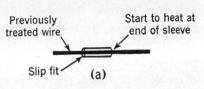

The glass apparatus is prepared for the seal by blowing out a hole in it. This hole is always slightly smaller than the bead. A tiny hole may be blown in glass by exposing a spot to the side of a pointed flame and blowing strongly at the same time. When possible, it is preferable to make the metal-glass seal in a small tube, which can then be welded

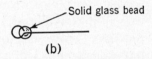

Fig. 35. Preparing metal wires for final glass seal. (a) Making a bead from a sleeve of glass. (b) Eyelet bead. Tungsten is too brittle to be bent into a small eyelet.

to the apparatus as in a T seal or Dewar seal. The final step is the fusing of the bead and the glass, which should be a glass-to-glass weld, as the platinum should not touch glass except at the original bead.

Though often stated to the contrary, it is possible to make perfectly satisfactory direct 774-platinum seals for use in liquids with wire up to about 20-mil diameter. No special technique is required, and the problem of electrodes in electrolytic cells drawing small currents, supposedly a rather difficult construction, is in reality very simple. With wire of this size, vacuum leaks are very small and can be stopped with a dot of sealing wax or de Khotinsky cement.

**Tungsten.** The wire, up to about 40-mil diameter, can be sealed directly to Pyrex No. 774 but requires careful annealing. Larger sizes are always first sealed to Nonex No. 772

or yellow "uranium" glass (Corning No. 332), which is then fused to the 774 apparatus.

The metal is first out-gassed by heating to white heat. It is then rubbed with a stick of solid sodium nitrite to clean it. If the application is correct, upon cooling and washing a shiny surface will result. The reaction between sodium nitrite and the metal is highly exothermic, and repeated application of the salt stick will keep the metal glowing hot and gradually wear it away. As a matter of fact, this method is the easiest and safest way to decrease the diameter of or put a sharp tip on tungsten, which is very hard and brittle.

A bead of glass is now fused to the wire, and this bead is sealed to the glass as with platinum. The actual bond between metal and glass will vary in color, usually being reddish-purple or brown. This color is presumably due to a thin film of oxide at the surface, formed during the beading process. However, overoxidation leads to a dark, porous interface which will not show the color of a good tungsten-glass seal.

Nonex No. 772 wets the metal beautifully, and many glass blowers prefer to make even small tungsten seals with it or uranium glass, which has much the same properties. Nonex No. 772 has a lower working range than 774 and also contains some lead, making it necessary to work at the tip of an oxidizing flame.

Tungsten can be brazed, though with difficulty, or constantan (advance) or nickel can be fused to it without flux. The tip of a tungsten wire extending from a vacuum system should be fused to another metal (preferably before the glass seal is made) to stop off any capillary leak path between the fibers which constitute the metal wire.

**Molybdenum.** Glass seals to molybdenum are made in a manner exactly analogous to that used for tungsten seals. The expansion of the metal at low temperatures is very close to that of Corning glass No. 705AJ, which should be used. This glass is in turn sealed to 772 and then to 774. Uranium glass is sometimes used between the latter two. Molybdenum seals are very satisfactory if the metal, which oxidizes rapidly, is handled carefully. Too much surface oxidation gives a sticky layer at the seal which will not adhere.

**Kovar and Fernico.**[1] Kover and Fernico are alloys of iron, nickel, and cobalt which have very desirable properties

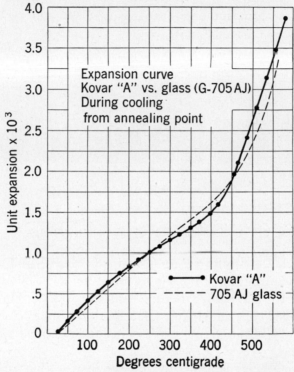

Expansion curve Kovar "A" vs. glass (G-705 AJ) During cooling from annealing point

●———● Kovar "A"
- - - - 705 AJ glass

Degrees centigrade

*After Bulletin KA, Stupakoff Ceramic & Mfg. Co.*
**Fig. 36.**

for sealing to glass. In Fig. 36 is shown a plot of the expansion of Kovar "A" as compared to Corning glass 705AJ. It will be noted that the marked rise in expansion rate of 705AJ in a short temperature interval, characteristic of all glasses (see Chapter I), is practically duplicated by Kovar

[1] Kovar is the trade name of a group of alloys developed in the laboratories of the Westinghouse Electric and Mfg. Co. The exclusive fabricator and distributor of Kovar is the Stupakoff Ceramic and Mfg. Co., Latrobe, Pa. Fernico is the trade name of a similar group of alloys made by the General Electric Co., Schenectady, N.Y.

"A," which will seal to it vacuum tight without strain. Very small wires may be sealed to 774, and intermediate sizes will seal to 772. The 705AJ glass should be sealed to 772 and then to 774, with perhaps an intermediate ring of uranium glass. Fernico is sealed to 705AO, giving vacuum-tight, unstrained joints, as their expansion characteristics are also practically identical. The AO glass is graded to AJ, and thence to 772, and so forth.

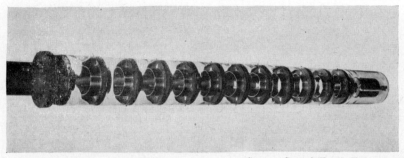

*Courtesy General Electric X-Ray Corp.*

**Fig. 37.   One million volt X-ray tube utilizing Fernico.**

The alloys may be easily machined, brazed, and soldered, but they are rendered porous by silver solder. They are not attacked by mercury. Before soldering, oxide film should be removed by immersion in a bath of hydrochloric and nitric acids, followed by a basic solution to neutralize remaining acid.

The main precautions to observe in working with Kovar and Fernico are to de-gas the surface and to oxidize superficially to form a favorable surface bond. If possible, the metal should be de-gassed in an induction furnace to prevent overoxidation, but it is satisfactory to vaporize surface gases by heating to a bright red in a mildly oxidizing flame and immediately form the glass seal. A good color for a seal varies from gray to brown; a black appearance is indicative of overoxidation. Such seals are still mechanically strong but may leak because of the porosity of the thick oxide coat.

Kovar and Fernico are surprisingly easy to handle in the laboratory. They may be sealed to the proper glasses internally and externally in tubular shapes, in wires, ribbons, and other forms. No special precautions other than ordinary good annealing practice need be taken. Indeed, a certain amount of strain seems to increase the mechanical strength of a seal, and in certain cases cooling in still air is the recommended procedure. However, extensive working at high temperatures is to be avoided.

When a great deal of glass-to-metal sealing must be done, or when metal vacuum systems must be used, as in physics laboratories, Kovar and Fernico are outstanding contributions of the last decade. They can be supplied as sheet, rod, wire, tubing, cups, eyelets, flanges, and other forms. A typical product, a complete Kovar-glass assembly for insulated hermetic sealing, is shown in Fig. 38.

**Pinch seals; Dumet.** Fine wires after degassing may be sealed to glass without beading by inserting the wire in a hot glass tubing end and pinching the opening shut with a forceps or pressing between carbons or transite. Such seals are usually strained, especially if the angle between the glass sides is very acute, but will work quite well on thin wires. Commercial thermionic-tube metal seals up to 1 mm to soft glass are often made this way with Dumet, a copper-sheathed iron-nickel alloy.[2] Dumet wire up to 10-mil diameter can be pinch sealed to 774, though Nonex glasses are easier to handle.

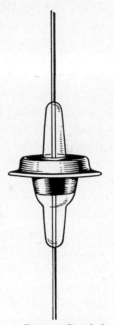

*Courtesy Stupakoff Ceramic & Mfg. Co.*

**Fig. 38. Kovar electrode hermetically sealed to and insulated from Kovar flange.**

---

[2] Dumet is the trade name of the alloy made by the Cleveland Welds Works, Cleveland, Ohio, and is used extensively for lead-in wires on electric lights. According to H. D. Blake of the Lamp Department, General Electric Co., Nela Park, Cleveland, Ohio, the present type of Dumet wire was developed during World War I to take the place of platinum and platinum alloys in lead-in wires, and is described in U.S. patent 1,498,908. An earlier patent of importance is U.S. 1,140,136.

**Housekeeper seals.** In 1923, Housekeeper[3] demonstrated that thin sections of metals with large expansion coefficients could be sealed to practically any glass, provided that the metal had a low yield point and was wetted by the glass. Only two metals, copper and platinum, meet this requirement practically, though in theory any metal that is thin enough can be used. Platinum can be sealed vacuum tight to lead glass and liquid tight to Pyrex in small sizes, so that Housekeeper techniques are not usually required. However, the seals described below for copper can also be made with platinum. The two general rules for a successful Housekeeper-type seal with copper are that the metal, where sealed, must be at no spot more than 15 mil thick, and that, if glass passes over a metal end, the latter must be feathered off to a smooth knife edge. Thus, to make a copper ribbon seal, a wire is hammered down to less than .015 in. thickness, the edges are feathered off, the wire is cleaned and treated, and then a pinch seal is made. Sectional views of ribbon seals are shown in Fig. 39.

Where available, OFHC (oxygen-free, high-conductivity) copper should be used. It is cleaned by scrubbing in an ammonium carbonate solution, and must be de-gassed. Since the melting point of copper is only 1083° C, preheating is a ticklish procedure and requires practice. After the initial heating, the hot metal may be dipped in a borax solution and heated again. This treatment should produce an even, deep-red copper borate film which wets glass well.

Soft glass to copper seals have the advantage of low working temperature so that there is very little danger of melting the copper while the glass is quite fluid, or of oxidizing the metal at the edge of the seal so badly that it is porous and weak. Pyrex No. 774 seals are difficult because the glass has such a high softening point and also does not wet the copper easily. Nonex No. 772 is much better in both ways and should be used, the 772 lead being sealed to 774 in the usual manner. The metal should be red hot while the seal is being made to insure a good bond.

---

[3] Housekeeper, W. G., *Elect. Engineering*, **42,** 954 (1923).

The finished seal *after cooling* should be bright orange or crimson at the interface. This color is presumably due to cuprous oxide, which does not form a sharp crystal boundary with copper. Black or dark color, which is due to cupric oxide, invariably designates a failure. Dark red color, more like copper borate, is doubtful, often indicating leaks. A bright yellow like that of pure copper itself is a sign of an

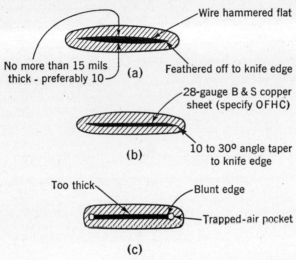

Fig. 39. Cross-sectional views of Housekeeper copper ribbon seals. (a) On section of a wire hammered flat. (b) On copper sheet. (c) Certain to crack or leak for any of three related reasons.

excellent seal but is usually obtainable only with Nonex No. 772.

**Disc seal.** The manipulations involved in making a disc-type seal are fairly simple, but the glass must be properly set up. Fig. 40 shows the operations involved. The disc is 15-mil sheet or less and should be large enough so that glass has no chance to pass over the edge. The metal can be trimmed later if desired. The hole is put in the center merely so that blow control need not be used at both ends and is not necessary. The glass on one side is required to balance the distortional stresses on the copper resulting from the seal on the other side. The excess may be removed by cutting when cold or by heating with rotation and then pulling and blowing simultaneously to produce a very thin section, which may be shattered, and the end may then be bordered.

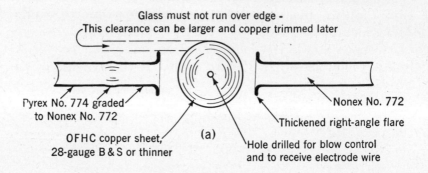

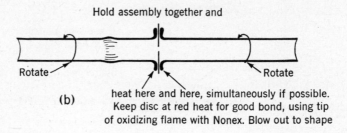

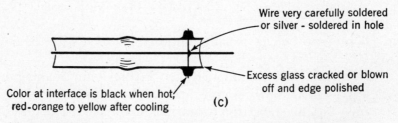

Fig. 40. **Disc seal.** (a) The assembly. (b) Making the seal. (c) Finished.

To seal a metal wire or small tube on, the copper is drilled to size, the required metal inserted, and the joint silver soldered with a tiny flame after the whole area has been preheated. This job is at best ticklish and is a big drawback to the use of the disc seal. It is possible to solder the lead to the disc before making the seal, but the joint may melt while the seal is being made if one is not careful.

**Tubular seals.** Housekeeper tubular seals may be internal, external, or both. In making the initial bond, it is advisable

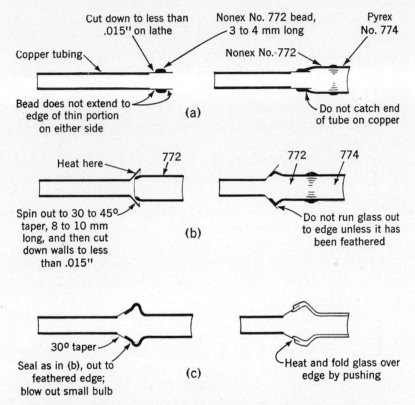

**Fig. 41. Tubular Housekeeper seals.** (a) External seal. (b) Internal seal. (c) Sealed on both sides, the most difficult to make but the most satisfactory.

The seal in (b) may be ringed with cane on the outside, making it analogous to a disc seal.

to heat the *copper* near the seal (this statement is contrary to that found in other descriptions of Housekeeper seals, but the author's experience has been that it is the best procedure). The best but most difficult type of seal is that in which the glass is sealed on the inside along the wall up to the edge, which is feathered, and then folded over to seal also to the outside.  This seal is very badly strained, as are all Housekeeper seals, but is the best from the standpoint of freedom from leaks and mechanical strength.  Some of the techniques that can be employed in making tubular Housekeeper seals are indicated in Fig. 41.

As a final word, a strong precaution concerning the handling of copper should be added.  It is an excellent heat conductor and can cause serious burns.  The use of thick asbestos alone as an insulator is not sufficient and also gives rise to irritating smoke from the filler.  Two glass sleeves centered with pre-burnt asbestos should be used, and even under these circumstances the copper cannot be heated for too long a period.

**Solder seals; platinizing.**  In some instances it is desirable to solder metal to glass.  If properly done, the resultant seal is as strong as the glass itself and is recommended in cases in which high temperatures are not encountered and soft solder is not objectionable.

The glass is thoroughly cleaned with cleaning solution, rinsed with water and finally 95 per cent ethanol.  Platinizing solution, the recipe for which is obtainable from any chemical handbook, is painted on, and the glass is heated to 650° C for a few minutes in a furnace.  If no furnace is at hand, the glass may be held above an oxidizing Meker flame.  A bright film of platinum should result.  The metal is soldered to this film with a soldering iron (not with flame heat), using solder of 60-40 composition and a flux of 5 per cent ammonium chloride in glycerol.  The soldering iron should not touch the platinum, which, though bonded to the glass, may stick to the iron and be pulled off.  It is preferable to platinize the inside of a bordered glass end so that the outside of the metal may be tinned in advance and a ring of solder may be added around the resultant well.  Two or three coats of platinum may be used on the glass if desired.

**Iron, chromium, nickel.**  Extremely thin sections of these metals can be sealed to glass by Housekeeper techniques. For a more detailed description of such seals and also other aspects of glass-to-metal seals, the reader should consult Housekeeper and others.[4]

**Porcelain.** Electrical porcelain can be sealed to glass if the expansion coefficients are closely matched. The techniques are similar to Kovar seals.[5]

[4] Housekeeper, W. G., *Elect. Engineering*, **42**, 954 (1923); Hull, A. W., and Burger, E. E., *Physics*, **5**, 384 (1934); Hull, A. W., Burger, E. E., and Navias, L., *J. App. Physics*, **12**, 698 (1941).

[5] Bahls, W. E., *Elect. Engineering*, **57**, 373 (1938).

# CHAPTER XI

## Finished-Equipment Exercises

IN addition to the examples presented along with the development of the text in the preceding chapters, there are any number of useful pieces of apparatus which also serve as glass-working exercises. This chapter includes a selection of these, approximately in order of their difficulty. Explanatory and constructional details are given where necessary, largely through the use of sketches. The examples have been chosen for their general utility, though no attempt has been made to cover every field in which blown glass is usable.

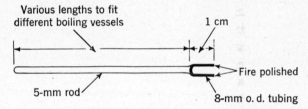

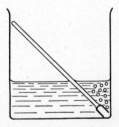

Fig. 42. "Anti-bumper." Twenty or thirty of these, in varying lengths, can be made in less than an hour.

**"Anti-bumpers."** These simple little devices are remarkably efficient in preventing bumping of a solution being heated and are a very rudimentary exercise in glass manipulation. They do not contaminate a solution, as boiling stones

100

may, and are easy to clean.   The method of construction of the design shown in Fig. 42 should be obvious.

**Manometer-barometer.**   An absolute manometer and barometer which has the advantages over the common U type of being sturdier, less subject to breakage, easier to clean, having less danger of contamination, and of assuring that one limb is completely evacuated, has been described by Professor Robertson.[1]   The manometer, shown in Fig. 43, is very simple to make and practically foolproof in use. The original article should be consulted for details of filling the manometer with mercury.

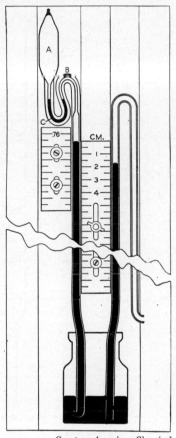

**Vigreaux column.**   Among the simple fractionating devices is the Vigreaux column, shown in Fig. 44.   To make an indentation, a spot of glass is heated strongly and then pushed in with a piece of wax-coated, pointed 50-mil nickel or tungsten wire or a pointed $\frac{1}{16}$-in. carbon rod.   If these are not available, a file handle can be ground down to the desired diameter.

**Air condenser.**   The surface of a condenser tube may be increased in many ways.   One of the more common designs utilizes

*Courtesy American Chemical Society and G. R. Robertson*

**Fig.   43.   Combined manometer-barometer.**

large indentations in the glass, as diagramed in Fig. 45.   These indentations are made by heating the glass at a spot until it has begun to shrink and then sucking gently.   An adapter is sealed on the end.   The condenser may be made water cooled, either by sealing on a water

---

[1] Robertson, G. R., *Ind. Eng. Chem. Anal. Ed.,* **17,** 238 (1945).

jacket, as in the condensers in Chapter VII, or by slipping over a tube with a side-arm near either end and fitted with rubber stoppers.

**Y cut-off.** Where the use of stopcock grease is objectionable in gas-handling systems, it is often possible to employ

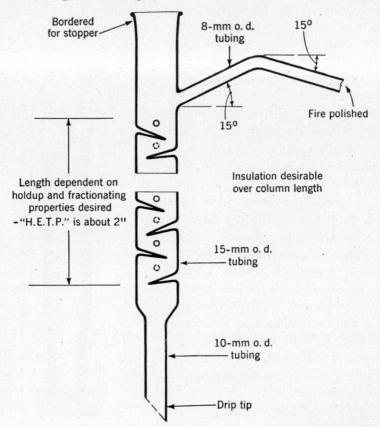

Fig. 44.   Vigreaux-type fractionating column.

a mercury valve. To save mercury and also to prevent it from bumping over when the two arms are under unequal pressure, ground float valves can be used. The mercury reservoir and pressure-control vessel are preferably attached to the tail tube through a ring seal, as shown in Fig. 46, but can also be sealed through a rubber stopper.

Construction of the cut-off involves using the hand torch,

working solid glass, and grinding, in addition to other basic techniques.

**Melting-point bath.**  A modified Thiele heating bath for determining melting points,[2] shown in Fig. 47, uses mechanical rather than thermal current stirring.   The bath is an exercise in making a closed circuit with fairly large-bore tubing and

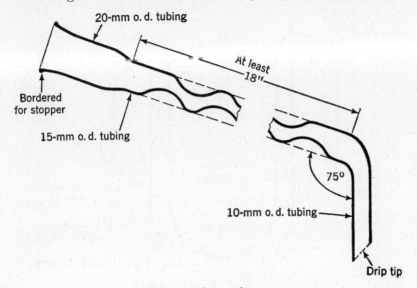

Fig. 45.   Air condenser.

must be annealed carefully.   For best results, the right arm should be electrically heated and the whole bath insulated, except for a viewing window by the melting-point tube. The stirrer is described in Chapter IX; the melting-point tube is described in Chapter III.

**Glass aspirator.**  This device is commonly used in the laboratory and is a good exercise in blowing ring seals. Many designs have been described, and the worker may want to experiment to find others more efficient than the two sketched in Fig. 48.   Two precautions are necessary: (1) A thick-walled, wired-on rubber hose must be used to attach

[2] Avery, S., *Ind. Eng. Chem.*, **20**, 570 (1928).   Another modification is that of Conte, E., *Ind. Eng. Chem. Anal. Ed.*, **2**, 200 (1930), which has a ring-sealed nozzle for air stirring.   See also Hershberg, E. B., *Ind. Eng. Chem. Anal. Ed.*, **8**, 312 (1936).

the aspirator to the water tap; and (2) a trap must be used between the system and aspirator.

**Double-surface condenser.** When very volatile solvents, such as diethyl ether, are encountered, ordinary reflux

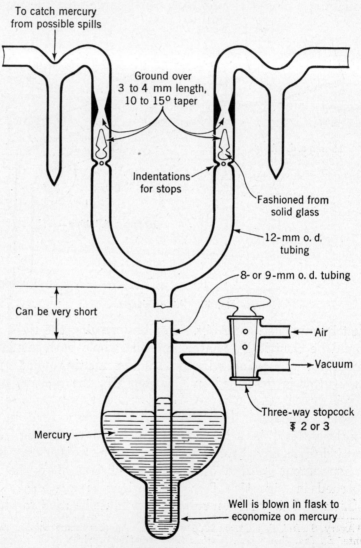

**Fig. 46. Y cut-off.** Shown with cut-off open and pressure in the reservoir slightly greater than in the system.

condensers are inadequate. A double-surface condenser, in which the vapor is constrained to travel in an annular ring, is far more efficient than the common types. The design shown in Fig. 49 includes the inner cone of a $\overline{\overline{S}}$ 24/40 joint

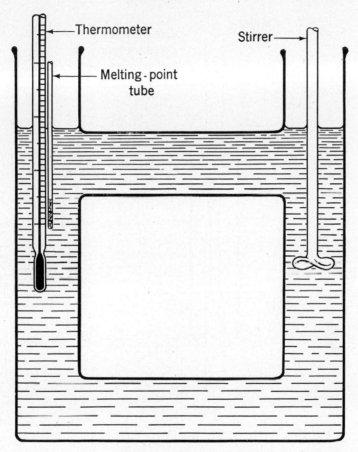

Fig. 47.   Avery's modification of Thiele's heating bath for determining melting points.

with drip tip for joining to a boiling or extractor vessel and also three solid glass feet on the water inlet of the cold finger. The feet are an aid in one method of construction, making the final ring seal easier by preventing wobble of the water-inlet tube.

**McLeod gauges.** The McLeod gauge in one form or another is indispensable for the absolute measurement of low pressures. Standard types are adequately described in many places. Fig. 50 shows a more extended variation for measuring pressures over a wider range.

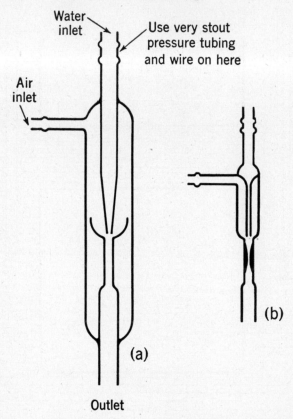

Fig. 48. **Water aspirators.** (a) Larger aspirator. (b) Smaller model, requiring only one ring seal.

**Tipping McLeod.** Another type of McLeod gauge deserves notice. It is the tipping type, as shown in the frontispiece and in Fig. 51. This type requires no backing vacuum or pressure. It is compact, small, fast to read, and as accurate as the standard kind. It requires two closed circuits of tubing, as opposed to one in the standard type. These circuits should not be closed—that is, the final seal made—

on the straight tubes, but rather at the side welds.   This point is particularly important for the capillary reference, which should first be sealed at both ends to ordinary tubing before being bent or sealed in the gauge.

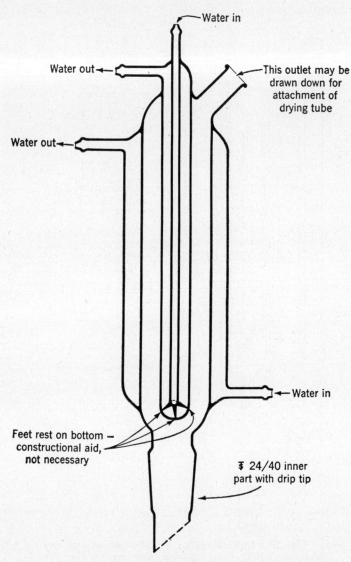

Fig. 49.   Double-surface reflux condenser for very volatile solvents.

The ground-joint swivel is surprisingly sturdy and easy to manipulate. If desired, the gauge may be mounted on a mechanical swivel, communicating with the vacuum system by means of a thick-walled rubber tube.

**Calibration.**  Two quantities must be known to calibrate a McLeod gauge—the volume of the measuring bulb, and

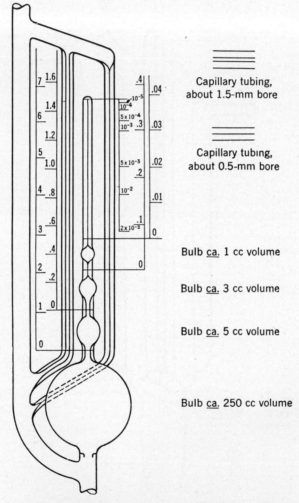

Capillary tubing, about 1.5-mm bore

Capillary tubing, about 0.5-mm bore

Bulb ca. 1 cc volume

Bulb ca. 3 cc volume

Bulb ca. 5 cc volume

Bulb ca. 250 cc volume

Fig. 50. McLeod gauge with four linear and one quadratic scales, giving pressure measurement over the range $<10^{-5}$ to $>7$ mm Hg.

the volume per unit length of capillary.   The former is easily determined with water before the bulb is sealed into the system, and the latter is usually measured by weighing a piece of the same capillary stock as that used in the gauge, adding a pellet of mercury, measuring its length, and weighing the capillary plus mercury.   The density of mercury at room

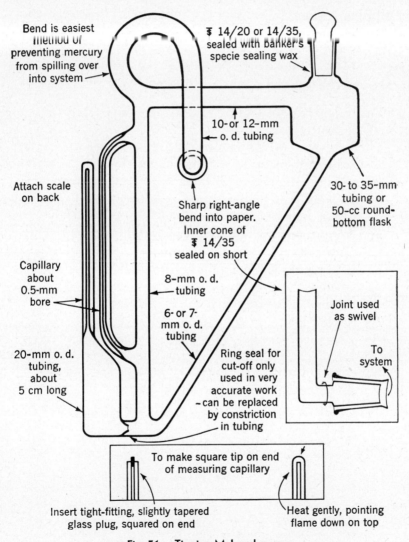

Bend is easiest method of preventing mercury from spilling over into system

₮ 14/20 or 14/35, sealed with banker's specie sealing wax

10- or 12-mm o. d. tubing

Attach scale on back

Sharp right-angle bend into paper. Inner cone of ₮ 14/35 sealed on short

30- to 35-mm tubing or 50-cc round-bottom flask

Capillary about 0.5-mm bore

8-mm o. d. tubing

6- or 7-mm o. d. tubing

Joint used as swivel

To system

20-mm o. d. tubing, about 5 cm long

Ring seal for cut-off only used in very accurate work – can be replaced by constriction in tubing

To make square tip on end of measuring capillary

Insert tight-fitting, slightly tapered glass plug, squared on end

Heat gently, pointing flame down on top

Fig. 51.   Tipping McLeod gauge.

temperature is 13.6 gm per cc to three significant figures, whence the volume per unit capillary length is given by

$$\text{cc per mm} = \frac{(\text{wt. Hg} + \text{capillary} - \text{wt. capillary}) \text{ in gm}}{13.6 \cdot \text{length of Hg thread in mm}}.$$

In reading the gauge, the mercury is usually brought to the same level in the reference capillary each time. With a tipping gauge, this involves filling with just the right amount of mercury, which can be determined by experiment. This method of reading gives rise to a "squared" or "quadratic" scale. The usual height in the reference capillary is that of the top end of the reading capillary.

Let $v_b$ denote the volume of the measuring bulb, in cubic centimeters,

$v_l/l$ denote the volume of the capillary per unit length, in cubic centimeters per millimeter (the $l$ is added in the denominator for dimensional consistency),

$p_s$ denote the pressure to be measured in the system, in millimeters of mercury,

and $h$ represent the difference in height between the two capillary levels, in millimeters. This is also the pressure in the capillary, in millimeters of mercury, since the pressure in the reference capillary is very small compared with it.

By Boyle's law,

$$p \cdot v = \text{constant}.$$

Substitution, the small capillary volume compared to the large bulb volume being neglected, gives

$$p_s \cdot v_b = h \cdot \frac{v_l}{l} \cdot h,$$

whence

$$p_s = \frac{v_l \cdot h^2}{l \cdot v_b},$$

or

$$h = \sqrt{\frac{v_b \cdot p_s}{v_l/l}}.$$

If the mercury is brought to the same level in the measuring capillary each time, we have, using the same nomenclature,

$$p_s \cdot v_b = h \cdot \frac{v_l}{l} \cdot d,$$

where $d$ is the distance from the top of the measuring capillary to the mercury level in it.   Then

$$p_s = \frac{v_l}{l} \cdot \frac{d}{v_b} \cdot h,$$

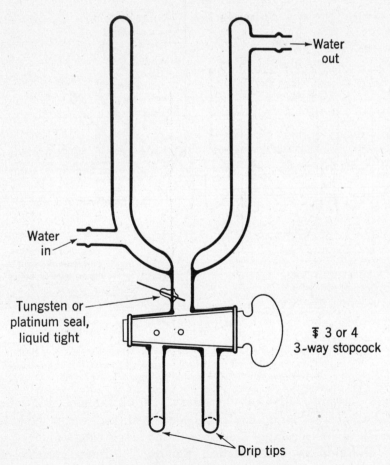

Fig. 52.   Water-jacketed electrolysis cell.

giving the "linear" scale, which is less accurate at low pressures.   It cannot be used with a tipping gauge.

**Electrolysis cell.**   An apparatus for electrolysis, employing a mercury cathode, is shown in Fig. 52.   The cell has

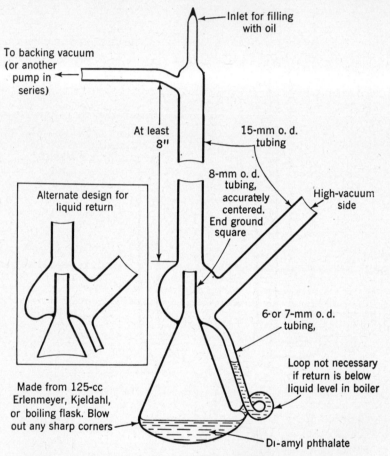

Inlet for filling
with oil

To backing vacuum
(or another
pump in
series)

At least
8"

15-mm o. d.
tubing

8-mm o. d.
tubing,
accurately
centered.
End ground
square

High-vacuum
side

Alternate design for
liquid return

6- or 7-mm o. d.
tubing,

Loop not necessary
if return is below
liquid level in boiler

Made from 125-cc
Erlenmeyer, Kjeldahl,
or boiling flask. Blow
out any sharp corners

Di-amyl phthalate

Fig. 53.  Simple up-jet oil-diffusion pump.   The diffusion chamber design may be proportionally enlarged for greater pumping speeds, but the ratio of boiler to nozzle cross-sectional areas should not fall below 3.

many uses in analytical chemistry.   From the glass blower's standpoint, it is interesting because of the water jacket, which involves a large Dewar seal and small ring seal.

**Diffusion or condensation pumps.**   A great variety of so-called diffusion pumps have been described in the literature,[3] and many other workable models have doubtless been made in various laboratories.   Many of these, however, are difficult to make, some of the multistage pumps being perhaps the acme of the scientific glass blower's art.   In this section one mercury and one oil pump are described.   They are

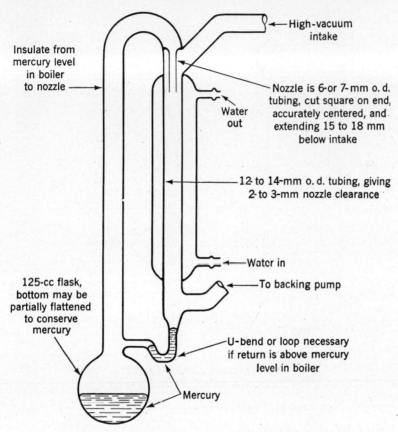

Insulate from
mercury level
in boiler
to nozzle

High-vacuum
intake

Nozzle is 6-or 7-mm o. d.
tubing, cut square on end,
accurately centered, and
extending 15 to 18 mm
below intake

Water
out

12- to 14-mm o. d. tubing, giving
2- to 3-mm nozzle clearance

125-cc flask,
bottom may be
partially flattened
to conserve
mercury

Water in

To backing pump

U-bend or loop necessary
if return is above mercury
level in boiler

Mercury

Fig. 54.   Water-cooled down-jet mercury diffusion pump.

both single-stage pumps.   The geometry of two or three jet pumps is critical, and for the average technician it is wiser to put two pumps in series, if saving of power is not important.

**Oil pump.**   The little oil pump shown in Fig. 53 needs no cooling of any kind.   It is the simplest pump possible,

---

[3] See, for example, Strong, J., *Procedures in Experimental Physics*, Chapter III, Prentice-Hall, Inc., New York, 1944.

from the glass blower's standpoint.  The cut-off pressure is small, about 0.2 mm Hg.  For good vacuums, two pumps in series should be used.  The nozzle clearance is not critical and may be as little as 1.5 mm, since the condensing oil runs down the sides of the outer tube in a thin film.  Diamyl

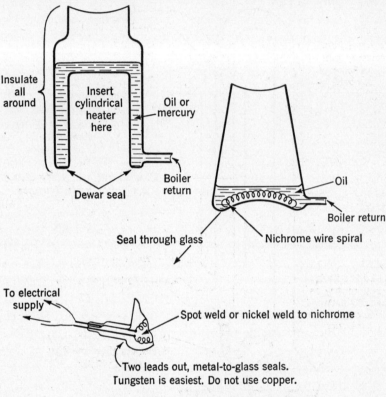

Fig. 55.  Boiler designs for diffusion pumps.

phthalate is a suitable oil, though other phthalates, sebacates, or refined naphthenic-base petroleum oils can also be used. Heat input on these oil pumps should be regulated so that a sharply defined condensing ring of oil appears about 15 mm above the jet.

**Mercury pump.**  The pump illustrated in Fig. 54 is in general use at the University of California at Berkeley, the actual dimensions having been standardized for service-ability over twenty years ago.  The clearances in the nozzle area may be varied somewhat without affecting the general performance greatly; it will operate over a wide heat input range; and it does not "cut off" until the backing pressure is well over 1 mm Hg. Two such pumps in series will actually operate with a good water aspirator as backing vacuum.

**Pumping speed.** A large pumping speed is always desirable; yet in most instances with glass "static" vacuum systems the use of high-speed diffusion pumps is futile. For example, no matter how large the pump, two 4-mm bore stopcocks in series in a vacuum line will cut its pumping speed to approximately 0.5 l per second.[4] Furthermore, the time required to achieve the limiting vacuum of the pumps in a system is often more dependent on the rate of out-gassing of the walls than on the pumping speed.

**Heaters.** Figs. 53 and 54 show the pumps with boilers that should be heated electrically with a resistance coil wound flat or in a well. With such heaters, they will require up to 250 w. In Fig. 55 are shown two boiler designs which lower the heat input necessary. The Dewar-seal type of boiler requires only 100 w at most with an insert heater and can be used on any type of diffusion pump, though it is not desirable to use it in small oil pumps. The internal heater is the neatest type for oil pumps. The glass-metal seals are made by the techniques described in Chapter XI, and the heating element can be nichrome or even very thin tungsten. Less than 50 w are needed to operate the pump of Fig. 53 with such a heater.

In operation, all-glass diffusion pumps should be heat insulated or "lagged" with asbestos putty, rope, or tape from the boiler to the beginning of the condenser surface.

**The pumping station.** As a "final examination" for the glass blower, the construction of a high-vacuum pumping station covers practically all the manipulations commonly encountered at the glass bench and in addition offers an opportunity for the display of technical ingenuity and originality on the part of the worker. The portable pumping station

----

[4] Calculated from the expression given by Knudsen, M., *Ann. d. Physik*, **28**, 75, 999 (1908).

illustrated in the frontispiece is adequate for many purposes, though by no means uniquely so, and is described in some detail below primarily as a means of comparison with and discussion concerning alternative constructions.

The frame is made of ½-in. cold-rolled steel, brazed at the joints and painted black. The base (not shown) consists of two angle irons, brazed to the side rods and drilled, with a board set on them and held in place with countersunk bolts and nuts. The over-all dimensions are as follows: Base, 30 × 14 in.; height, 24 in. The brazed construction and small size give it sufficient rigidity so that no angle rods are required, and it is easily lifted and carried about when the glass is in place.

Larger, permanent frames require cross braces and are mounted on a table or low bench. Some metal work is so closely allied to glass manipulation that all glass blowers should familiarize themselves with the elements of metal handling; construction of a suitable vacuum-bench frame is in itself a good exercise.

The diffusion pump shown is of the up-jet oil type, being essentially a larger version of the pump shown in Fig. 53. The nozzle is 16-mm o.d., the condensing surface is 25-mm o.d., and the boiler is made from a 250-ml Erlenmeyer flask, wrapped with asbestos rope and heated with a simple flat external heater, not shown. Optimum heat input is 120 w. The only novel feature of the pump is the series of catchment lobes or alembics, which serve to increase the efficiency of the condenser a little and, more important, partially to fractionate the pump oil so that the higher vapor-pressure fractions of the oil are trapped in the annular wells of the lobes. If the pump were to be used under conditions in which the oil was frequently exposed to air and hence much cracking were to occur, a drain tube would be sealed to the uppermost alembic. Details of the method of blowing a catchment lobe are shown in Fig. 56.

It should be noted that there are as few constrictions as possible in the main pumping line, and that large stopcocks are used (except from oil pump to backing pump, where a

large valve is unnecessary).   Even so, the line has undoubt-
edly cut down the speed of the diffusion pump considerably.

The vacuum-type stopcock ($\overline{\$}$ 8) is sealed in as an
integral part of the trap.   An alternative procedure would
be to have the valve in the line and perhaps to use a $\overline{\$}$ 29/42

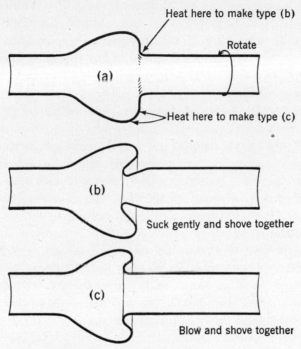

Fig. 56.  Alembics.   Bulb (a) is first blown, and from
it the lobe (b) or (c) is made.

conical joint on the trap so that it can be cleaned easily.   It
is important not to reverse the inlet and outlet of the trap,
for large amounts of vapors then condensing in it might plug
the inner tube.

The side line leading to the tipping McLeod need not be
large.   As shown, the gauge will read the pressure of the
pumping system only.   For reading the pressure elsewhere,
another lead should be sealed on beyond the last stopcock
and both entrances controlled by a three-way stopcock.   The
necessary stops for the McLeod are in this case clamps for
the various pieces of apparatus, the clamps fortuitously being

placed about right. They are sleeved with rubber tubing where the gauge can touch them. The scale has not yet been attached to the McLeod gauge, which reads $9 \times 10^{-3}$ mm Hg, representing the pressure obtained by the mechanical fore pump when the system was first tested for leaks. After one hour's operation of the diffusion pump, the McLeod indicated approximately $5 \times 10^{-5}$ mm, about the limit of the gauge, and, when liquid air was placed around the trap, a "stick vacuum" (mercury sticking at the top of the measuring capillary) was obtained. Such behavior is typical of static pumping systems.

Even though a "stick vacuum" was obtained, there are too many stopcocks and joints for really high-vacuum work, in which the parts should be fused together, with as few stopcocks as possible, or preferably mercury cut-offs with liquid-air traps for mercury vapor, and as much glass as possible baked out *in vacuo* at 350° C. The system shown will not achieve its base pressure (ultimate pressure without pumping load due to vapor pressure of the lubricants and the slow rate of cracking of the pump oil) until it has been pumped continuously for a week or so, for the stopcock lubricants, walls, and sealing wax will continuously out-gas. On the other hand, the use of stopcocks, joints, and sealing wax greatly facilitates handling, dismantling, and cleaning operations.

# Glossary

## A. Nomenclature of Glasses

THE nomenclature of glasses is so important and fundamental to the understanding of this book that a complete discussion of terminology is given here. Soft glass, lime-soda glass, and the like, unless further qualified, are general terms and refer to glasses with expansion coefficients of the order of 80 to 120 $\times$ $10^{-7}$ per degree C. Lead glass refers to a soft glass containing lead. However, in the past 25 years, the use of Corning glasses has become so widespread in the laboratory that some confusion has resulted regarding their designations.

"Pyrex," "Nonex," and "Vycor" are registered trade-marks owned by the Corning Glass Works, Corning, N.Y., under which are sold over one hundred different glass compositions, each identified by number. The trade-marks denote origin and have no composition significance. Particular Corning glasses can be identified only by number, since more than one glass may be found under each of the trade-marks. Thus the glass popularly known to scientists as "Pyrex" is correctly called "Pyrex-brand chemical-resistant glass No. 774" or abbreviated as "774"—*not* as "Pyrex," since other Pyrex-brand glasses are different from it, whereas "774" is unique.

In this book, Pyrex-brand chemical-resistant glass No. 774 is referred to as Pyrex No. 774 or 774. When the term "Pyrex" alone is used, it refers to Pyrex glasses as a collective whole.

"Nonex No. 772" or "772" refers to the glass popularly but erroneously known in the laboratory as "Nonex." No confusion is likely to arise from the naming of other sealing-in glasses, which are ordinarily spoken of by number—as, for example, 705AJ.

All glasses referred to by number in this book are manufactured by the Corning Glass Works.

## B. Alphabetical List of Terms Used

ABRASIVE.   Hard material, either powder or solid, used in grinding away surfaces.

ALEMBIC.   Lobe for catching liquid running down the walls of a tube.

AMORPHOUS.   Having no definite crystalline pattern.   The term may be applied to glasses and also to certain solids like lampblack (carbon).

ANNEALING.   Slow cooling to relieve thermal strains set up in hot glass.

ANNEALING POINT.   Temperature at which a glass can be annealed in 15 min.   The viscosity at this temperature is $2.5 \times 10^{13}$ poises.

"ANTI-BUMPER."   Device for eliminating bumping or violent boiling in a solution being heated.

ANNULAR ORIFICE.   Open space between two coaxial tubes.

ASPIRATOR.   Simple liquid-flow entrainment pump for gases.

AXIS.   A straight line, real or imaginary, on which an object may be symmetrically rotated and still present the same appearance.

"BACKFIRE."   Condition in which flame velocity is greater than gas flow rate, so that flame burns back into torch.

BAROMETER.   Device for measuring the pressure exerted by the earth's atmosphere.

BEADING.   Applying a bead of glass around a metal wire.

BLAST LAMP.   Burner with inlet for compressed air and oxygen.

BLOW TUBE.   Length of light rubber tubing used to transmit air pressure from mouth to glass being blown.

BORDERING.   Flaring and thickening a tubing end.

BRAZING.   Soldering with brass.

BRUSH FLAME.   A diverging flame with wide, not-well-defined end.

BULGING.   Putting a small bulb in tubing, or merely increasing its o.d. slightly at one place.   See also MARÍA.

BUNSEN BURNER.   Laboratory burner using aspirator effect of flowing gas to inject air into flame.

BURNER. Apparatus for producing a controlled flame.

B & S. Arbitrary scale for diameters of circular cross-sections. No. 28 B & S wire is 0.0126 in. in diameter.

CALIPERS. Measuring device for inside and outside dimensions.

CANE. Cylindrical solid glass.

CAPILLARY. Small-diameter bore. Unless otherwise stated, capillary tubing refers to thick-walled tubing.

CATCHMENT LOBE. See ALEMBIC.

CHUCK. Clamp or holder.

COEFFICIENT OF EXPANSION. See THERMAL EXPANSION.

COHESION. Tendency of parts of the same material to stay together.

COLOR TEMPERATURE. Color due to radiation which is common to all bodies. A dull red becomes apparent about 650° C in daylight, changing to orange, yellow, and white as the temperature is increased to about 1400° C.

CONDENSATION PUMP. See DIFFUSION PUMP.

CROSS-FIRES. Two burners or flames pointed at each other.

CRYOPHORUS. Device for demonstrating heat of vaporization.

CRYSTAL. A solid with definite, repeated micro structure.

CUT-OFF. Valve for gas flow utilizing a liquid which can be raised or lowered past the joint of a Y.

DEVITRIFICATION. Process of crystal formation from a glassy or vitreous material.

DEWAR SEAL. Weld in which an inner and outer tube are joined at one end without any extension of tubing.

DIDYMIUM. Mixture of two rare earths, neodymium and praseodymium, used in glass-blowing goggles because of its selective absorption of sodium light.

DIFFUSION PUMP. Pump for gases utilizing molecular bombardment, by vapor from a boiling liquid, of gases in a system.

DISC SEAL. Glass-to-metal seal in which a thin disc of metal is sealed between two glass tubes.

DOWEL. Solid cylindrical rod.

DUMET. Copper-sheathed iron-nickel alloy used for lead-in wires in incandescent lamps.

ELASTIC.   Temporarily deformable under influence of an outside force; upon withdrawal of this force, an elastic substance assumes its original shape.

L.   Right-angle bend.

END SEAL.   Welding two glass tubes together endwise.

FAN TIP OR FISHTAIL.   Fitting for Bunsen burner which changes flame to long, thin shape.

FERNICO.   Cobalt-iron-nickel alloy with desirable properties for sealing to glass.

FLAME.   Flowing gas which is hot enough to emit light.

FLANGING.   Making a large flare, usually perpendicular to a tubing axis.

FLARING.   Widening an end of glass tubing.

FLOW TRAP.   Apparatus used to trap out materials flowing in a system.

FOCUSED FLAME.   Pointed flame with well-defined edges.

FUSED.   Properly defined as "melted," but often used to mean melted and recooled.

GLASS.   "An inorganic substance in a condition which is continuous with, and analogous to, the liquid state of that substance, but which, as the result of having been cooled from a fused condition, has attained so high a degree of viscosity as to be for all practical purposes rigid."[1]

GRADED SEAL.   Seal between glasses with different expansion coefficients, such as lead glass to Pyrex No. 774.

GROUND JOINT.   Two sections of glass ground to a close fit, either conically or spherically, and usually lubricated to produce a vacuum-tight seal.

HAND TORCH.   Small, portable torch.

HEAT CONDUCTION OR TRANSFER.   The diminishing of a temperature difference between two objects.

HOUSEKEEPER SEAL.   Glass-to-metal seal depending on deformation of very thin metal sections to relieve expansion stresses on cooling.

H. E. T. P.   Height of an equivalent theoretical plate.   This is the length of a fractionating column corresponding to an effi-

---

[1] Morey, George W., *The Properties of Glass*, p. 34.   Reinhold Publishing Corporation, New York, 1938.

ciency in distillation such that the liquid at the bottom and the vapor at the top of this length are in equilibrium.

INORGANIC. Not containing carbon.

I.D. Abbreviation for "inner diameter."

JIG. A contrivance to hold work in place as desired.

KIDNEY. Very thin glass blown out on end or side of tube in preparing it for a seal.

KOVAR. Cobalt-iron-nickel alloy with desirable properties for sealing to glass.

LAMP. See BURNER and BLAST LAMP.

LAMPBLACK. Amorphous carbon deposited by flame with insufficient oxygen (reducing flame).

LATHE. Machine for uniform and precise axial rotation of materials.

LEAD GLASS. Soft glass containing lead.

"LEADING A CRACK." Breaking large glass by applying a hot tip of cane on a scratch mark extending beyond edge of crack made by the previous cane application.

LEAK TESTER. See TESLA COIL.

LEHR. Annealing oven.

LIME GLASS. See SOFT GLASS.

LOCOMOTIVE. Mammoth multiple Meker-type burner with special air or oxygen injector.

McLEOD GAUGE. Low-pressure manometer working on Boyle's law principle.

MANDREL. Machinists' term for a long cylinder about which something is wrapped or turned.

MANOMETER. Device for measuring pressure, usually of gases.

MARÍA. Slang term often used by glass blowers to designate a bulge.

MEKER BURNER. Large laboratory burner built on Bunsen principle, but with a wire mesh or grid on top to make flame wider and more uniform.

MELTING POINT. That temperature at which the crystalline and liquid forms of a substance are in equilibrium—that is, can both coexist without tendency to change.

MESH. Degree of fineness of an abrasive powder.

MIL. Thousandth(s) of an inch.

MOUTHPIECE. Thickened glass tubing or pipe stem attached at mouth end of blow tube.

ORGANIC. Containing carbon.

O.D. Abbreviation for "outer diameter."

PADDLE. Flat plate of carbon, iron, or nickel used in shaping hot glass.

PERIPHERY. Circular or spherical surface.

PINCH SEAL. Glass-to-metal seal in which hot glass is pinched down on wire or thin ribbon of metal.

PLASTIC. Permanently deformable under application of an outside force.

PLATINIZING. Applying a thin coat of platinum on glass by reducing a special chloroplatinic acid solution (platinizing solution) on glass by heating.

POISE. The c.g.s. (centimeter-gram-second) unit of viscosity. A poise is unit shearing resistance of a fluid film which separates two horizontal plates, one being moved across the other. The viscosity of water at 20° C is approximately one centipoise (0.01 poise); of glycerin, 10 poises.

QUARTZ. A crystalline form of silicon dioxide.

RING SEAL. Common term for triple seal.

ROLLERS. Adjustable wheels arranged to permit rotation of glass tubing resting on them as a bearing.

SILICA. The chemical silicon dioxide.

SODA GLASS. See SOFT GLASS.

SOFT GLASS. Glass made with a relatively high percentage of lime or soda. Also applied to low-softening-range, high-expansion glasses.

SOFTENING POINT. Arbitrary temperature defined in terms of the rate of elongation of a glass fiber under its own weight. The viscosity at this temperature is $4.7 \times 10^7$ poises.

SOFTENING RANGE. Temperature interval over which a glass softens and becomes plastic.

SOXHLET EXTRACTOR. Device for continuously passing fresh liquid through a solid to extract certain parts of that solid.

SPARK COIL. See TESLA COIL.

SPLICING TORCH. Small hand cross-fire torch.

"SPOTTING." Heating only a small part of a glass join at a time.

"SQUARING OFF." Making even and smooth the jagged end of a piece of tubing.

STOPCOCK. Glass valve, usually lubricated with grease.

STRAIN. Force tending to deform or break an object.

STRAIN POINT. Temperature at which a glass can be annealed in 16 hr. (arbitrary). The viscosity at this temperature is 4. $\times 10^{14}$ poises.

SWIVEL. Small brass tube fitted with inner freely rotating tube, allowing work to be rotated without twisting attaching rubber hose.

$\mathcal{F}$. Symbol for standard taper (interchangeable) ground-glass surfaces on stopcocks, glass stoppers, and joints.

T SEAL. Weld in which one glass tube is joined at right angles to another tube.

TESLA COIL. Instrument which gives a high-voltage discharge from a pointed electrode.

THERMAL EXPANSION. Enlargement of a material due to heating. The coefficient of linear thermal expansion is given as $(1/l_0)[(l - l_0)/(t - t_0)]$, where $l$ is a length and $t$ a temperature.

TORCH. See BURNER.

TORQUE. Bending force.

TRANSFORMATION TEMPERATURE. Temperature at which the thermal expansion coefficient of a glass begins to increase markedly.

TRANSVERSE. At right angles to an axis.

TRAP. See FLOW TRAP.

TRIPLE SEAL. Weld in which a glass tube is sealed to, but also extends through, another piece of glass.

VACUUM TESTER. See TESLA COIL.

VIGREAUX COLUMN. Column for fractional distillation of liquids in which the surface is increased by placing sharp indentations in the glass tubing.

VISCOSITY. Degree of resistance to plastic flow. See POISE.

VITREOUS. Glassy.

WELDING ROD. Small-diameter glass cane.

YIELD POINT. Force or stress applied to an object necessary to deform it.

# Index

## A

Air, compressed, for heating, 8
Air condenser, 101, 103
Alembic, 116, 117
Annealing:
  burners for, 8
  methods of, 5–6
Annealing oven, 5, 18
Annealing point (*table*), 2
"Anti-bumper," 100–101
Asbestos paper, 15, 19
Asbestos tape, 15, 20, 21
Aspirator, glass, 103, 106
Avery, S., 103

## B

Bahls, W. E., 99
Ball-and-socket joint, *see* Spherical
  joint
Barometer, 101
Beeswax, 18
Bellows, expansion, 76–77
Bench, glass blower's, 19–22
Bends:
  angle-seal type of, 30, 74
  large, 73–74
  sharp, 30, 74
  silica, 85–86
  spiral, 30, 75
  techniques in making, 29–30, 32,
    40–41
  T-seal type of, 30, 74
  U, 30
Blast torch, 9
Blowing:
  cutting glass by, 25
  involving one piece of glass, 36–41
  techniques in, 37
Blow tube, 15, 20, 21
Bomb tube, 33
Bordering, *see* Flaring
Brace (*see also* Clamp):
  flow-trap, 54–56
  ring-seal, 53

## Bulb:

Bulb:
  auxiliary, in test-tube end, 31
  in end of tube, 39
  in middle of tube, 39–40
Bulge, 34–35
Bunsen burner, 8
Buret, repairing, 32
Burger, E. E., 3, 99
Burners (*see also* Torches):
  glass, 11
  placement of, 22
  types (*see also under specific types,
    as* Bunsen, Cross-fires, etc.),
    8–11

## C

Calibration of McLeod gauge, 108–112
Calipers, 14, 20, 21
Cane:
  cutting glass with, 24
  welding, 13–14, 20, 21
Capillary tubing, techniques of ma-
    nipulation of, 72–73
Carbon tools:
  dowels, 18, 20, 21
  rods, 18, 20, 21
  use of, in flaring, 27–28
Carborundum:
  equipment, 18
  use of, in grinding, 82
Cell, electrolysis, 111, 112
Cement, de Khotinsky, 70
Chromium, 98–99
Circuit, closing a, 67–68
Clamp (*see also* Brace), for spherical
    joints, 80
Closing a circuit, 67–68
Coil:
  glass, methods of making, 75
  Tesla, 69
Column, Vigreaux, 101, 102
Condensation pumps, ii, 112–115
Condenser:
  air, 101, 103
  double-surface, 104, 107